A Balance of Trust

'Hindhead is Safe'

The story of Fifty Years
in the history of
Haslemere and Hindhead

---

during which
The National Trust
is founded

Introduction

In 1995, The National Trust celebrated its centenary. One of the founders, Sir Robert Hunter, lived in Haslemere, Surrey, and so it was appropriate that the Trust's southern region decided to mark the occasion by supporting the idea of a community play to be performed in that town, relating to the Trust's foundation.

Rather than cover the story solely from a national perspective, we gave it a distinctly regional bias, looking at about half a century of local history between the arrival of the railway at Haslemere and of the motor car at Hindhead. These were critical events by any measure, and conveniently embraced the Trust's significant year, 1895.

Haslemere had sunk into lethargy since the first Reform Bill robbed it of its Members of Parliament in 1832. It was, quite literally, on the road to nowhere, until the railway in 1859 opened up the area as a commuter belt. Some would say this shook a bit of life into the district; others that it marked the end of the old village and the start of an inevitable progression towards urban sprawl.

It put extra pressure on the use of land. Acts of Enclosure in the mid 1850s had allowed common land to be parcelled up and sold to rich 'incomers,' who often fenced it off and denied entry to others. The railway now provided a ready means of access from London and elsewhere, and added to the incentive to buy and build. In short, the area was earmarked for invasion.

In this it was not unique. It was the fight to protect open spaces in other parts of the country which eventually led to the creation of the National Trust, but the district around Haslemere, and in particular Hindhead Common, was to benefit quickly from the organisation which Hunter had helped to found.

The local newspapers in 1905 confidently declared 'Hindhead Safe' when the common was bought at auction by a group of public-spirited local residents and conveyed to the Trust. This feeling was given further support in 1907 when Parliament passed an act under which the Trust was given the power to declare its land as 'inalienable.' This designation protects the property from compulsory purchase by a local authority or by a ministry - it can only be taken by a special Act of Parliament.

Today, of course, the pressure comes from the motor vehicle. With dual carriageway along the whole length of the A3 from London to Portsmouth except for the few miles across Hindhead, it seems that something has to give as the 'irresistible' force of the juggernaut meets the 'immovable', or at least 'inalienable,' property of the Trust.

So is Hindhead truly safe? Will it be forced to wear a deep scar, like Butser Hill and Twyford Down - will it be tunnelled under like Tyndall's cherished Alps - or will some completely novel solution to the problem emerge?

At the time of writing, we can only say: "Watch this (open) space!"

John Owen Smith
Headley, 1995

Robert Hunter and Jonathan Hutchinson were both dedicated men...

To a great extent they worked towards the same end. Hunter preserved the commons and open spaces for the good of the nation; and Hutchinson wished to encourage healthy minds and bodies, including the need for people to get out and live in these spaces.

But if people lived there, the spaces would no longer be open. This is the dilemma explored in 'A Balance of Trust.'

Our story begins in the present time. Three National Trust wardens meet for a coffee inside the oldest hostelry on Hindhead....

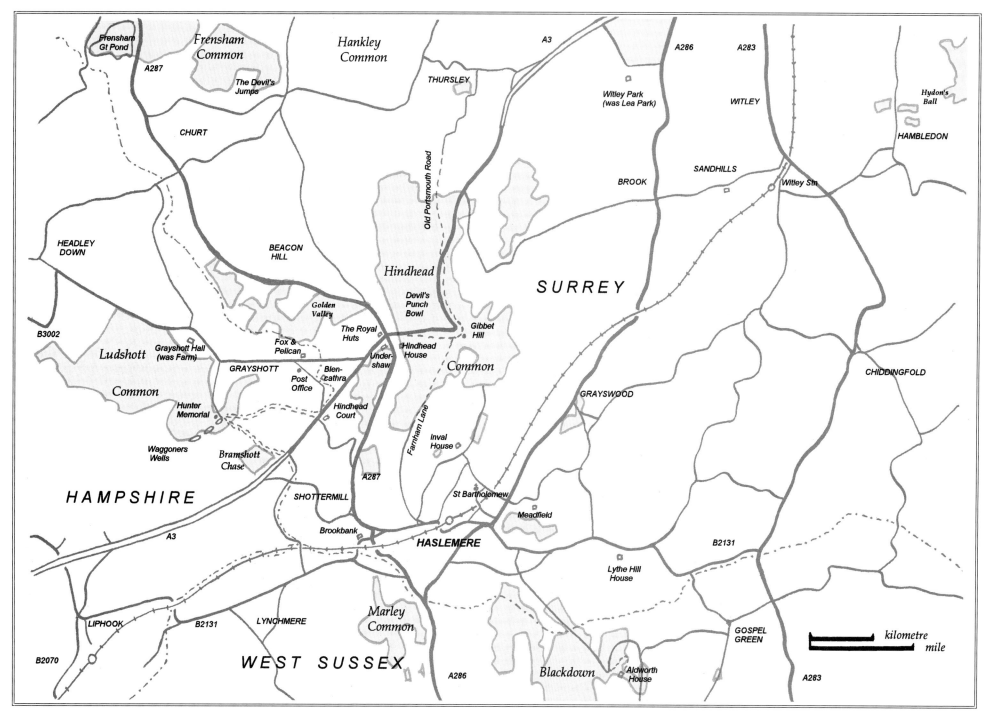

Modern map of the area, showing local National Trust property and places mentioned in the book

Inside the 'Happy Eater' at Hindhead

They came in dripping wet, and eased themselves slowly into spaces on either side of the table. Through the steamed-up window, the traffic outside still queued in the rain at Hindhead crossroads. Tony shrugged off his jacket and let it hang over the back of his chair.

"What'll it be?" Miranda was quick off the mark today - trade was slack, and she was there beside them, pad and pencil in hand, before they'd even had time to settle.

"Three coffees please, love," Tony replied without asking his colleagues. Andy nodded in mute approval. Chris looked vacantly through the window. "You know," he said, "people used to flock here in their hundreds once, to breathe the fresh air. Purest air this side of the Alps, they said."

The Royal Huts, Hindhead

The name 'The Huts' is thought to derive from some old huts made of turfs and thatched with heather, used to store whortleberries (or bilberries) which were sent to London for dyeing purposes.

It was mentioned by William Cobbett in 1822 when, on his unhappy ride from Headley to Thursley, he "came out on the turnpike some hundred yards on the Liphook side of the buildings called 'the Hut.'"

The last publican to brew his own ale here was John Ellistone, and when he left in 1893, Ben Chandler, who was in the brewing trade, took the hotel into the 20th century and started the first motor-bus service from Hindhead and Grayshott to Haslemere. By that time the inn was called 'The Royal Huts Hotel'.

Later this century it became one of the 'Happy Eater' chain of restaurants.

"Not no more," said Miranda indifferently - "will that be all?" Sensing the answer was 'yes', she tore off their order, slapped the scrap of paper on the table, and disappeared into the secret bowels of the kitchen.

"Not no more," - Tony mimicked, his eyes following her.

"That's progress for you," said Andy. "Once this was the wildest place in southern England. Took your life in your hands travelling over Hindhead then you did."

Chris grinned. "Now you're lucky to get over it at all - I've seen people fall asleep waiting for those lights to change."

"Odd sort of place, Hindhead, when you think about it," Andy mused. "A stopping off and going through place - not somewhere you'd come to specially. Time it made its mind up what it is."

"Seems a stupid place to put a road anyway," growled Tony. "I mean, all the routes you could take to get from London to Portsmouth, and they had to stick it straight over the top of the biggest hill around."

"P'raps they fancied the view," suggested Chris.

"Can't enjoy it these days anyway, unless you go on foot," said Andy. "Wasted on the through traffic, it is."

"More likely they didn't fancy the mud in the valleys," Tony replied.

"Still, those were the days, weren't they?" said Andy, with a sort of faraway look in his eyes.

Chris looked at him sideways - "What were?" he asked.

"More homely in lots of ways ...." Andy left the statement hanging in mid-air, and in his imagination travelled back in time nearly a century and a half. They were in the same room, but now it was the bar of *The Huts* public house....

In the bar of 'The Huts', Hindhead, 1854

"Not much business for you gentlemen here tonight - the weather's seen to that." William, the landlord, addressed his remarks to the three tradesmen seated in the bar - the night's only occupants - a carrier, a broomsquire and a milkman.

"There'll be the Portsmouth coach through before too long," replied Harry the carrier.

"If it's not got bogged down at Thursley," added Joseph the broomsquire, with some relish.

The Huts, Hindhead, circa 1890

"Hoping for some customers going down to Haslemere then, Harry?" asked the landlord.

"Why else would I be here with me cart?" Harry replied more sharply than he intended.

"Easy, Harry." Eli the milkman was the peacemaker of the group.

"Sorry I'm sure," William protested, "only trying to be civil. Can I fill your pots?"

Joseph drained his - "Aye, I reckon I could do with another one." The others followed suit, and William came over to take all three tankards back to the bar.

Harry attempted to excuse his outburst. "Business is tailing off - are you not finding it at *The Huts*?"

"There's as many coaches using the road as there ever was," William replied philosophically, pouring the pints.

"You wait though," said Eli, "there's folks say they're going to build a railway down in Haslemere."

William had heard it all before - twenty-five years or so ago the first railway in the country had been opened - now, in the mid 1850s, they were building them all over the place. They'd come out from London as far as Godalming, and Haslemere was threatened next - on a direct line to Portsmouth. "People will still use coaches," he said, "they're accustomed to them - too many accidents happen on the railways."

"Don't you be so sure, William," said Joseph. "Times change, and not for the better these days." He remembered how some other broomsquires had been thrown off their land by an enclosure three years ago. Then turning to the milkman with a twinkle in his eye he said, "They'll be bringing your milk in by railway before long too, Eli."

"Where they going to keep the cows?" replied Eli, thinking this would end the argument.

"Where are you going to keep them if they comes along and enclosures you?" retorted Joseph.

"Enclosures down Highcombe? They couldn't do that, it's common land down there."

"Doesn't seem to stop them," said William, coming back with the drinks. "If them with money want a bit of ground, common or not, they just get Parliament up in London to give a nod and, wallop, they've got a fence round it faster than you can say 'gate post.' Still, so long as I get the trade..."

"All over Frensham parish now - I've seen it happening," said Harry. "They'd best be careful they don't lose more than they gain. Aren't you worried they'll turf you off Joseph? Where would you make your brooms then?"

"There'll be broomsquires here for some time yet, don't you fret - we're a wily breed. Doesn't old Moorey supply the Queen's mother herself - up to London in his cart he goes, right to the palace door."

"Doesn't trust anyone else to take them for him," said Harry with feeling.

"More than once he's sold the horse and cart too, and had to walk home," said William. "Unless he finds a friendly carrier to bring him back," he added, looking at Harry.

Eli had got the wrong end of the stick again. "Sold them to the Queen's mother? His horse and cart?"

The Kings Arms, Haslemere High Street in 1887

"No Eli." Harry spelt it out for him. "The Queen's mother buys his *brooms* - he sells his horse and cart to whatever fool will give him money for them."

"Broomsquires are an institution round here," declared Joseph, "along with heath and birch - always have been and always will be."

"Amen to that," agreed William.

"Hold on," said Eli, making up for his dim wits with sharp hearing. "Here she comes - I hear the coach."

"It'll be on the straight run in from the Sailor's Stone," said Harry airing his professional knowledge. "Still a few minutes away."

"When did you say they were starting that railway?" asked Joseph casually, but more concerned than he wanted to let on.

"Oh, just talk I reckons," said Eli, "just a rumour."

William shook his head as he returned to his bar, "No, I'm told there's navvies due to move into Haslemere shortly."

"Be no end of trouble if they do," said Harry. "They'll be about as welcome as a plague of locusts. Seen 'em with my own eyes I have - rough load of..." But Eli interrupted again. "Pick up your goods, Joseph - she's about here."

The three men drained their pots quickly and made for the door to meet the coach. "Be seeing you, William," shouted Joseph.

"Aye," said William, coming to collect the pots, "and good luck to you all."

Haslemere High Street
just after midnight, early Sunday 29th July 1855

Saturday was always a difficult night for Inspector Donaldson, with the pubs having to close at the stroke of midnight and the drinkers inside not wanting to go home. On days when the railway navvies got paid, it was doubly bad. Still, he'd managed to keep the town within the law so far - not bad with a total police force of two men, himself and Constable Freestone.

Tonight, though, there seemed to be a small gang in the *Kings Arms* more intent on trouble than usual. He'd been polite but firm when he asked them to leave, but they'd not gone home, and when he and the constable emerged into the High Street again, they were waiting.

"Hey you!" The self-appointed leader of the gang, a man named Thomas Woods, moved unsteadily towards the Inspector. "Yes, you! You laid a hand on me just now."

Donaldson was outwardly calm. "You know the law - the pubs close at midnight on Saturdays."

Haslemere Town Hall, when used as a 'lock-up'

"At midnight is it?" railed Woods. "And that gives you the right to drag me from my drink does it? A drink I'd paid for with my own hard-earned money, building your railway."

"Go home peacefully, Woods, there's a good man, you'll feel better in the morning."

"Home? Who's going to make me go, then?" sneered Woods, squaring up to the two officers. "The entire Haslemere police force - two of you - just two men!"

Donaldson had enough experience of handling drunk and disorderly behaviour to realise it was mostly bluster, but his constable was less well seasoned and, thinking his superior was about to be

hurt, moved quickly between the two of them and pushed Woods over.

Woods fell, in his drunken state, then picked himself up and started to attack the constable, who defended himself vigorously with his truncheon. This broke with the force of the blow, and Woods fell to the ground again.

The Inspector felt that things were beginning to get out of hand. "Steady!" he shouted, trying to keep his voice even. "Now will the rest of you go home?"

"What've you done to him?" One of the gang bent over Woods, and the others joined him. "You've killed him, that's what you've done," said another. "Let's get him!" cried a third, and as one they turned and set about Freestone again.

Donaldson saw the time for bargaining had passed, and moved in to assist his constable, but at that moment Woods rose unnoticed from the ground and picked up a large iron bolt. Lifting it above his head, he ran up behind Donaldson crying, "All together lads!" and brought it down on the Inspector's head.

Both officers lay helpless on the ground. "Not so high and mighty now, inspector," yelled one of the men, stamping on Donaldson's ribs. "Nor your constable," gloated another, putting the boot into Freestone's head.

"Somebody coming!" cried a third, and the kicking stopped.

Woods stood above the prostrate forms for a moment longer. "You'll not be throwing me out of any more pubs, Inspector Donaldson," he muttered, and gave him a last kick in the face before following his workmates away, disappearing with them into the shadows.

Freestone, less severely injured, managed to rise to his knees. "Help!" His voice was pitifully weak. "Walter! William! Anybody! Help!"

Hesitantly, two or three law-abiding Haslemere residents appeared from their doors, still dressed in their night-clothes and looking round to make sure the coast was quite clear.

"The Inspector," Freestone said urgently, "he's hurt - he's badly hurt - can't you see?"

"You're not so good yourself," said one, "we'd better get Dr Bishopp."

"He's coming now," said another. And sure enough the good doctor arrived hurriedly with his bag, and in a similar state of undress.

"Look at the Inspector first, Doctor," said the constable.

"He's done for if you ask me," one of the onlookers said from a safe distance. The doctor looked around for assistance. "Will some of you help me get him home?"

"How is he, Doctor?" asked another. "Let's just get him back home," pleaded Dr Bishopp. "Gently now, can you take his legs? Someone help me with his arms."

"Will he live?"

"God knows, Mr Gibbs," the doctor replied sharply, "but we shall do our best," then more gently, "and we'll make his passing easy, if it comes to that."

Inspector William Donaldson

... died of his injuries during the night - the first Surrey policeman to be killed on duty. Woods and his companions were arrested and sent for trial at Kingston where they were found guilty, but only of manslaughter. Woods was given 20 years transportation - the others custodial sentences of up to six years each.

Donaldson was buried in Haslemere churchyard, but the grave is now unmarked. In 1995 a plaque was unveiled in his memory on the wall of the Town Hall.

Haslemere Railway Station, mid 1860s

John Wornham Penfold alighted from the first class compartment and saw the porter was already unloading his luggage. He looked at the other passengers on the platform to see if he recognised any faces - after all, this had been his home for a number of years before business commitments in London forced him to move away. Now with the railway running through, he was able to consider moving back here while still working in Town.

The faces were all new. Well, it had been a long time, and there were many incomers living here now - city workers - all thinking along the same lines as himself no doubt. The place would be different.

"The carrier's waiting out in the station yard, sir." The porter's call brought him back to reality and he turned to follow. As he did so a figure came in through the entrance and hailed him. "Mr Penfold, good to see you."

Penfold recognised the man - he was James Stewart Hodgson, one of the newcomers who had already started to make a name for himself in the area. They'd met before when Penfold had visited his father at Courts Hill.

"Back in Haslemere again I see," said Hodgson. "By the looks of the luggage you're here for a spell."

"I can make London in less than two hours by train, so I see no need to live there all the time now."

Hodgson nodded his approval. "Well, you must come round and visit us at Denbigh House. Mrs Hodgson will be delighted to see you again."

"Just as soon as I'm settled in."

"All loaded on the cart, Mr Penfold sir." The porter was standing by the exit.

"Ah, thank you." Penfold searched in his pocket to find a suitable coin for the man, then tipped his hat to Hodgson and went out into the yard.

As he did so, two men dressed in hiking gear arrived at the station entrance. Professors Jonathan Hutchinson and Hughlings Jackson, both London surgeons and the best of friends, had been taking the country air for a few days and were about to return home.

Hutchinson looked spry and ready for a good few more miles, and struck his stick against a pillar in satisfaction. "Two days' hiking does wonders for the constitution, eh Hughlings?"

His companion, by comparison, appeared jaded and weary, and sank thankfully onto one of the station benches. "You know I have no great love of the country, Jonathan. How you got me out in this wilderness I don't know."

Railway timetable, May 1864							
Direct Portsmouth							
Weekdays:						**Sunday:**	
W'loo	7.05	11.30	3.50	5.00	7.00	10.15	5.00
H'mere	8.46	12.53	5.13	6.26	8.37	12.01	7.20
P'mth	9.52	1.55	6.12	7.29	9.42	1.03	8.25
P'mth	7.40	11.00	12.00	3.00	7.10	7.10	6.15
H'mere	8.46	11.56	1.24	4.05	8.15	8.15	7.20
W'loo	10.20	1.15	2.55	5.30	9.52	10.05	9.00

His friend turned to him with a glint in his eye. "Had to get you fit for your wedding day, old man. If I'm to be your best man, I have the responsibility to see you're up to it."

"Up to what?" replied the prospective groom gloomily. "I'll have no energy left for anything at this rate. I'd have been far better off sitting at home reading a good novel."

"Hah! Don't know what you find in such trash. I can see I'll have to cultivate your mind as well as your body. Poetry now, *there's* the stuff to savour."

"You and your poetry," Jackson said, and began to recite one of the few pieces he knew, *"Beside the lake, beneath the trees..."* Hutchinson cut him short. "Not Wordsworth again, Hughlings, *please*. How about the new laureate, Tennyson - now there's a man with a real gift for words."

"And he reads novels," rejoined Jackson with some glee.

"Does he indeed?" said Hutchinson in surprise.

"So I'm told." Jackson yawned. "I shall be glad to get on that train and go to sleep."

"It's the quality of the air round here," said his friend, jocularly. "Bracing."

Jackson was not impressed. "I'd never choose to build my own house out here in the wilds like some have."

Hutchinson disagreed. "Marvellous place to live. Good for the health - children would thrive here - plenty of spare land for all - some beautiful areas, quite unspoilt."

Jackson could see the irony in this. "They'd be spoilt if all your people moved in and started building though, wouldn't they Jonathan?"

Hutchinson had heard this argument before, and replied quite sharply, "We've no right to prevent city folk sharing the benefits of the countryside, Hughlings. I've a mind to come here myself one day, and I'd be happy for as many as possible to follow me."

It was as near to an argument as these two cronies ever got, and the sound of a distant train whistle put an end to it. Hutchinson checked his watch. "One twenty-four - right on time," he said with satisfaction. "You can set your clocks by the railway these days."

Jackson rose to his feet unsteadily. "You will wake me at Waterloo, won't you?" he asked pleadingly.

A Room in London, 1866

George Shaw Lefevre had once in his early 20s photographed the siege of Sebastopol and ridden on horseback from Vienna to Constantinople. Now aged 34, he had a more sedentary role as MP for Reading and had founded the Commons Preservation Society the previous year. Today he was in earnest discussion with Sir Henry Peek, who had offered prizes for the best essays on the subject of *Commons and the best means of preserving them for the public.'*

"You say your competition has brought in a fine crop of entries, Sir Henry? I must say it was a most generous act of yours to offer the prize money."

"We must all do what little we can, Mr Lefevre," replied Peek. "Your Commons Preservation Society is still young and needs all the support it can get."

"But you offered £400 for the best essay - that's no small amount," Lefevre said with admiration. "And you have selected a winner, I gather."

Sir Henry smiled. "In fact six entries have impressed me enough to put yet more money forward - I'm having them all published at my expense." Lefevre was doubly impressed. "The winner was a Mr Maidlow," continued Sir Henry, "but I was also very much taken by the entry of a young chap named Robert Hunter."

"In what way?"

"Difficult to put my finger on it - you'll have to read his entry yourself. I have a printer's draft of it here." He passed the paper to Lefevre and continued, "You may also be interested to learn that he is about to become articled. I mention that, because I hear that you are presently looking for a good and sympathetic solicitor to act for the Society."

It was true. Their present solicitor had been offered a post by the Government in the Office of Works, and this would make it impossible for him to be impartial if he remained with the Society. Lefevre saw that Sir Henry had offered a potential solution.

"Robert Hunter?" he said, "I'll certainly bear the name in mind."

The Tennysons with sons Lionel & Hallam, circa 1862

Grayshott Farm, May 1867

Mrs Anne Gilchrist worked too hard, according to her friends. Widowed at the age of 33, she had completed her husband's major literary work on Blake three years after his death, and brought up her four young children as best she could - always worrying that she was not doing the best for them. Now aged 39, she had suddenly found a new project to involve herself in.

She had been waiting at Grayshott Farm all morning for the carrier to appear, and was glad when he eventually pulled up at the gate. She knew him slightly, a local man, and went out to greet him. "Mrs Tennyson will be glad the furniture has arrived," she told him, "we were beginning to think it was lost on the railway."

Harry grinned. He was used to such comments and, in his laconic way, largely ignored them. Getting down from the cart he went to unstrap his load.

"Where would you like it put, ma'am?" he asked.

Mrs Gilchrist sighed. Where indeed? She had hoped Mrs Tennyson would be here herself to make the decision, but they had been called away unexpectedly to visit Hallam who had fallen ill at Marlborough. She looked at the cart. "It will have to go into the front room for the time being," she told him. "I still have to work out the final arrangements. Come in and I'll show you where."

He followed her into the house. "Quite a thing, having someone so famous living round here," he said, "how come he chose Grayshott?" Mrs Gilchrist hesitated before answering. Mr Tennyson had been very anxious that his arrival should not be widely advertised, but since the local population appeared to have found out, there seemed little harm in being honest with the man.

"He likes the peace and quiet," she replied, leading him through the door, "and hopes to get away from the day trippers who are plaguing him on the Isle of Wight. He is renting this farmhouse while he looks for somewhere to build a new property."

Harry nodded wisely at this. "He'll not be at Grayshott long then."

"For a good year I should think," she said - then out of interest asked the man, "Do you read his works?"

Harry blushed a little. "I'm not much of a reader, ma'am - didn't get the schooling."

She felt ashamed for asking. "I'm sorry."

"But I've heard some of his stuff being read by others." Harry then brought the conversation round to something he did know about. "I imagine he'll like walking out on the commons just here. Real beautiful it is, what with the nightingales singing and all the wild flowers out in the woods and all."

Mrs Gilchrist smiled. "It was that which led me to choose the place for him." Then she remembered there was work to be done and added more brusquely, "Now, will you bring in the furniture?"

"Yes ma'am. I gets carried away I do, that's my problem."

Harry whistled as he went out to start unloading, and almost collided with a gentleman coming up the path. He had an Irish accent, and asked who was home. "You'd better come and talk to the lady," said Harry, and led him back indoors.

"Gentleman here for Mr Tennyson, ma'am," he announced. Then, tipping his cap, he went out again leaving them together.

"This is Mr Tennyson's house?"

"It is," replied Mrs Gilchrist with some hesitation.

Sensing her distrust, the man extended his hand to her. "My name is Allingham, William Allingham."

It had a certain familiarity, but she remained cautious. "I'm afraid Mr Tennyson is not at home today. Was he expecting you?"

"No. I was visiting Farnham yesterday, and thought I'd search out his house while I was in the area."

"I have heard him talk of you I believe," she said, seeking confirmation.

"Oh indeed - we are friends of many years standing," he reassured her. "We are, and I hope I can say this without false pride, brother poets. But you have the advantage of me, madam."

"I am Mrs Gilchrist."

At this the man's eyes lit up. "Whose husband wrote the *Life of Blake*?" he exclaimed. She nodded - she really should not be surprised at one of Tennyson's friends making the connection.

"I have read the work - excellent, excellent," he cried. "Delighted to meet you," and at this he shook her hand vigorously. "Tennyson keeps good company here. Have you known him long?"

"Less than a year," she admitted. "He turned up, literally, on my doorstep last September asking for directions - he wanted to view a local beauty spot,

the Devil's Jumps, and I took him there."

"Was he impressed?"

"I'm afraid not. He was looking for some land to buy, and thought it a most desolate spot. 'Very dear at the money,' he said - 'What is the use of a number of acres if they will not grow anything?'"

"What indeed," agreed Allingham.

"I remember he was more impressed with the tremendous rain storm gathering behind us at the time."

Allingham laughed. "I shall search for a reference to it in his next work." Then, looking around, he asked, "Does this area suit him better?"

"It seems to suit all four of them. Mrs Tennyson says the smell of the heather has improved her health already, and Mr Tennyson has bought a copy of Morris's *British Birds* - he and the boys have been listening for fern-owls out on the common here."

The Nightjar or Fern-Owl

A night-flying bird with long hawk-like wings and tail, and grey-brown 'camouflage' plumage, which inhabits heathland at its borders with woodland. Its song after sunset, a very distinctive 'whirring' sound, gives the bird its name. Its silent flight at night on soft-feathered wings likens it to the owl. Also called the 'Goatsucker,' by Gilbert White and others.

Now returning to heathland near Haslemere after some years absence.

"So nobody is in?" asked Allingham.

"Lionel is here," she replied. "Perhaps he'd like to show you round." Allingham's face lit up, and she called out to the boy through the open window.

"Do they occupy the whole farmhouse?"

"The best part of it." He moved to examine one of the pictures on the wall, and at this moment an

energetic twelve year-old bounded into the room, nearly knocking him over.

"Mr Allingham! I didn't know you were coming," cried the lad.

"Nor did I till yesterday, Lionel. How are you?"

"All right," he said. Then, with enthusiasm, "Do you want to play football again?"

Allingham remembered times on the Isle of Wight when they had kicked a ball about in the garden. "Perhaps," he said, "if the old bones will let me."

"Come on." The youngster was already half out of the door. "And after that I'll show you where we're going to build a big house."

"Is it near here?" asked Allingham.

"The other side of Haslemere. Did you come in a pony chaise? We can go over in that."

"And you can give me a lift home on the way, if you would be so good," added Mrs Gilchrist.

"You have no transport?" asked Allingham in surprise.

"The walk here does me good," she said rather too quickly.

He sensed he was perhaps on delicate ground. "How far away are you?"

"Just down in the valley, in Shottermill - a couple of miles perhaps." She wouldn't mention the fact that the hills were steep and her health not of the best. She prided herself in her ability to cope. Allingham did not press the matter. "I'd be delighted," he said.

Lionel was getting restless. "Come on Mr Allingham, let's get into the garden."

Mrs Gilchrist smiled as the man disappeared through the door towed by the boy. "I'll see you both when you've finished," she called after them, then with a sigh went to help move the furniture in.

Haslemere High Street, July 1867

For Jane Hutchinson, this was a new world. Having lived in London for so long, the lack of such basic amenities as cobbled streets and gas lighting in Haslemere was a constant reminder to her that life in the country was different indeed. And as for the speech of the natives! Her eldest daughter, ten year-old Elsie, had complained that she couldn't understand what people were talking about. Jane had told her confidently that she would get used to it.

They had driven to the market a couple of hours ago with Jonathan. He had gone off on some errand or other, and she had just about finished doing the shopping.

Jonathan Hutchinson in 1862

"Look mama, a man selling brooms." Elsie pointed out the stall. "You said we needed a new one."

At the stall was old Joseph the broomsquire. He sat surrounded by heather and birch besoms, his weathered face and battered old hat just visible above the merchandise. Jane approached him with some trepidation. "One of your brooms, if you please," she said.

Joseph looked her in the eye. "They's be the best brooms you'll ever buy, ma'am - made by my own 'and they be."

Jane glanced down at Elsie, who was trying to stifle a giggle. "I beg your pardon?" she asked.

"Buy one o' these, ma'am, an' your floors'll be clean as a new pin an' no mistake."

Jane could only guess what he was telling her. "Just one, thank you," she said, loudly and distinctly. To her relief he seemed to understand and handed her a broom from under the counter, but she wasn't quite sure if he had told her the price. "How much did you say it was?"

"That'll be just thruppence, if y'd be so kind ma'am," came the rapid reply. To Jane it might as well have been in Swahili. "Oh yes," she said hesitantly, and offered him a number of coins from her purse. "Is this enough?"

"Thank'ee ma'am, that's just about right." By the look on his face he seemed satisfied. Almost forgetting to pick up the broom in her embarrassment, she turned and quickly made her way back across the mud of the High Street with her daughter. "*What* did he say?" she asked Elsie when they were out of his earshot. Elsie chortled out loud. "Never mind mother," she mimicked, "I'm *sure* you'll soon get used to it."

They were both still laughing when they met up with Jonathan. "Ah, there you are my dears," he said looking at them with a raised eyebrow. "Are you ready now to collect the fly and go home?"

Jane brought herself under control, as befitted her Quaker upbringing. "Yes husband, I think we are about finished."

"And you, Elsie - how do you like Haslemere now?"

Still suppressing giggles with some difficulty, Elsie replied, "I like it, father, but it's as if we're in a different country."

Hutchinson considered this answer with favour. "A different country? Yes, it might well be - but a healthier country, do you not think?"

A healthier country? Jane was not so sure. "But for the lack of pavements to walk on, gaslight to see by, piped water to drink ...," she started to reply, but her husband cut her short.

Jane Hutchinson with children Elsie & Jonathan, c. 1860

"Such progress will come in the fullness of time, when Haslemere is recognised for what it is - the centre of a beautiful and healthy location a mere hour and a half from London," he declared.

This reminded her. "Did I tell you we saw Mr Tennyson waiting on the railway platform as we arrived from London the other day?"

"He was looking very poetic," Elsie added, "with long hair and big black cloak and hat. Wasn't it exciting to see him?"

"Yes," said Jane, "and I hear he has just bought some land to build himself a new house on Blackdown."

Hutchinson nodded sagely. This was confirmation of what he had just told them. "As I said," he repeated, "Haslemere is starting to become recognised."

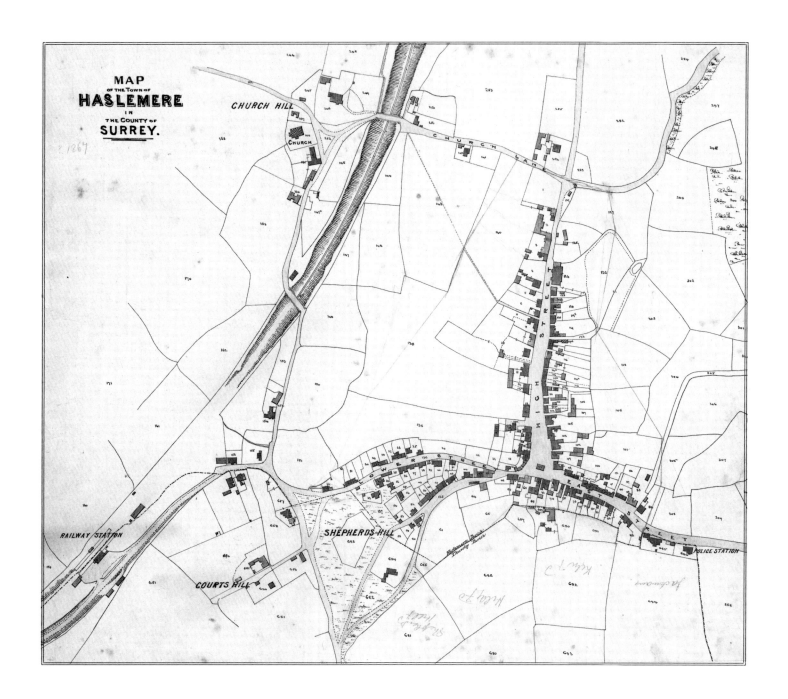

Map of Haslemere, circa 1867

Outside Haslemere Parish Church, 1868

It had been the first service to be conducted in St Bartholomew's since Haslemere had become a separate parish by separation from Chiddingfold, and the new rector, Mr Sanders Etheridge, met Hodgson and Penfold afterwards. Hodgson was the first to greet him. "Congratulations Mr Etheridge. A new parish will bring a new vitality to the village I'm sure."

St Bartholomew's church before July 1870

"The *village*?" Etheridge was taken aback by Hodgson's use of the word when referring to Haslemere. He thought he had come to a small market town.

"Some insist on calling Haslemere a town," said Hodgson, "but to me it's a village and will always remain so."

Penfold broke in, "You are a man of progressive ideas I believe, Mr Etheridge."

The rector thought for a while. "In all ways which may be of benefit to the town," he replied - then with a nod to Hodgson, "I mean village - yes I would say so, Mr Penfold."

The latter had an ulterior motive. "As you know," he said, "I am surveyor to the Goldsmith's Company, and I believe we should consider reconstructing the Parish Church, enlarging it to give us a building more appropriate to the needs of an independent parish."

Etheridge looked doubtful, and replied cautiously, "I should not wish to demolish the past in a rush to appease the future, sir."

"There's no fear of that if Mr Penfold is in charge of the plans," said Hodgson with confidence. "He takes great pride in preserving the original character of the buildings he restores. He has much professional expertise in these matters."

Etheridge was still not sure. "I hear that you have just pulled down Denbigh House, Mr Hodgson, and are constructing a new residence at Lythe Hill in Tudor style." He wondered if Hodgson's credentials were to be trusted.

Now it was Penfold's turn to provide support. "Believe me, Mr Etheridge, it was no great architectural loss. I have seen the plans of Lythe Hill, and it will be a great improvement."

"And you intend to 'improve' the parish church Mr Penfold?" said Etheridge with a touch of irony in his voice.

"We would not destroy anything that is picturesque or interesting," countered Penfold. "Will you allow me to show you some plans I have drawn up?"

This seemed reasonable to the rector. "I would be interested in them, yes. The church cannot appear to stand still while its flock marches forward. Shall you come to the Rectory with them tonight?"

"I should be delighted," said Penfold.

> #### St Bartholomew's Church, Haslemere
> *... was almost entirely rebuilt to Penfold's design between July 1870 and July 1871, using largely existing materials.*

St Bartholomew's church after July 1871

Shaw Lefevre's office in London, 1868

Shaw Lefevre, grim-faced, strode through the door to his office with Robert Hunter following two paces behind. He reached his desk and turned. "So we have a battle on our hands, my dear sir."

Hunter looked at the man, twelve years his elder. "I think we can handle it Mr Shaw Lefevre. You have, after all, already saved Hampstead Heath from the speculators."

"But now they're coming at us thick and fast." Lefevre began to count them off on his fingers: "Wimbledon Common, Wandsworth Common..." He stopped and sank into his chair. "Can we cope with so many law-suits together?"

The question appeared to have been flung at Hunter as a challenge. "We can," he replied calmly, "by employing diligence and resolve."

Lefevre looked long and hard at him. "You've got a lot of confidence, young Mr Hunter, for a man who's new to the business." Then after a moment's thought he added, "You put in long hours too - I can tell you're still a single man."

Hunter ignored this. "When you feel the cause is right, and others are with you, I believe it gives you the strength to keep going."

The other laughed briefly. "Well, 'keeping going' is what we have to do right enough, Mr Hunter, and we have strong allies in Huxley and Mill."

Robert Hunter on graduation in 1865

"That's true enough," Hunter agreed.

"And Wimbledon seems safe now, thanks largely to Pollock."

"But we need the ordinary men and women behind us as well," said Hunter, "as many as possible, to make representations on our behalf. Our Commons Preservation Society is an effective body ..."

"It was the first national conservation body to be formed in the country," Lefevre interjected, his tone sharp.

"Indeed," agreed Hunter, "and I believe it goes a long way to attracting the kind of support we must

have to fight the enclosures, but ..."

"But you don't think it goes far enough, eh?"

Hunter felt he should tread carefully, but was determined to push home his point. "It would be quite wrong of me to criticise the good work we are doing now. As you say, I am new to the problem..."

"A new broom," his senior remarked wryly, but Hunter continued, "... and I shall be giving our position a great deal of thought. We are, for example, lagging behind the rest of Europe and America."

Lefevre sighed and stretched his arms. It had been a long day and he was tired. "Then I suspect we have not heard your final word on the matter, Mr Hunter."

"I hope not, sir."

Here was an earnest and positive young man, thought Lefevre. He would need guidance of course, but given his head it would be interesting to see how far he could go. "I look forward to hearing your further ideas when we next meet, but now I must leave you - it is late, and I am expected home."

He took his coat and hat from the stand and started for the door. Hunter made no move to follow. "You are staying here?"

"I have one or two things to finish off."

"Then I shall say good night to you."

"Good night." Hunter was already contemplating the papers which he planned to read and make notes on before himself going home. It was a habit he was to continue for many years to come.

A Room in London, 1875

Seven years later, despite having been married and then widowed within three years, Hunter's keen legal mind had been the driving force behind saving Epping Forest from enclosure, an achievement which had brought the Society and its causes much good publicity.

Other organisations were now looking to the Society for a lead, and today Miss Octavia Hill and her young solicitor friend Edward Bond had come to discuss with Hunter the possibility of enlisting his help to their cause.

Miss Hill was not in the best of moods, having recently failed to save Swiss Cottage Fields from enclosure. While waiting for Hunter to appear, she was berating Bond about the situation.

"Nine thousand pounds, Edward," she almost shouted at him. "That's how much we raised - a substantial sum of money you'll agree."

"Substantial, Octavia, but not enough." Bond was well acquainted with her outbursts, and tried to remain calm in the face of the squalls. It was not always easy.

"By public subscription," she continued unabated, "surely a clear enough indication that the people wish to preserve these fields for public use, not have some speculator fill them with yet more bricks and mortar."

"Octavia..."

"It's the poor who suffer - surely the speculators can afford them some breathing space."

"Octavia, dear..."

"It's no use 'Octavia Dear-ing' me, Edward. There was a clear will among a considerable number of people in the area - and in the end they were ignored, because a rich man wanted to line his pockets even more."

"I agree it was unfortunate we couldn't make the final selling price...."

"Unfortunate, pah!" she almost spat back.

"But we did all that we reasonably could," he added limply.

Her big brown eyes almost flashed in their disapproval - a familiar sight to those who knew her, and usually a signal to stand well clear. "We sent letters, yes," she cried, "but what *action* Edward?" Her hand slapped the table to emphasise the word.

Bond knew he was unlikely to make any impact on her while she was in this mood. "Considering the short time we had..." he began.

Another slap. "These things will *always* come to us at short notice, Edward. We weren't sufficiently organised. We must be better prepared next time."

"And you feel this meeting with Hunter is a step in the right direction."

"The Commons Preservation Society has been established for ten years now and has a permanent organisation," she said, telling him what he already knew.

"But the Swiss Cottage land was not a common," he pointed out. This had been the nub of their problem.

"Which is why we need to encourage the Society to enlarge their scope." In her mind she had already made the decision for them.

Bond wanted to see the lie of the land first. "Hunter's position is?" he asked her.

"He's their solicitor - a young chap, about your age, but he knows his business - a real worker."

He hoped her last comments were not meant to be a slight on himself, but before he could reflect on this, the object of the compliments entered the room in person. Robert Hunter was indeed about his age, just turned thirty, and held out his hand in greeting.

"Ah, Miss Hill and Mr Bond - good day to you both. I trust you are well."

Shaw Lefevre in 1884

Octavia, as usual, answered for the two of them. "Thank you, Mr Hunter, we are well - but irate at our failure in the recent proceedings."

Hunter looked at her with understanding. "The Swiss Cottage Fields, yes. Sadly that matter is now beyond salvation."

"But for the future ..." Bond started.

"...we should like to have the weight of your Society behind us," Octavia finished for him, "we feel it would give us more chance of success."

Hunter had brought a sheaf of papers in with him, and these now lay on the desk. "I have seen your letter to our secretary," he replied, indicating the top of the pile. "Indeed I have read it through several times and made some notes."

Octavia was impressed at the man's thoroughness, but was in no mood to show it. Almost as though he had not spoken, she continued, "If you were to add to your objects 'the acquisition and dedication to the public of open spaces in or near London' - I feel it would not be inappropriate."

"And I am glad to say that I entirely concur with your views, Miss Hill," he replied. A look almost of satisfaction began to show on Octavia's face as Hunter continued, "I should be glad to draft a text to that effect for consideration by our committee."

As another solicitor, Bond thought that perhaps he should be more involved in this conversation. "You feel there would be no problem in it?" he asked.

Hunter spread his uplifted palms. "Problems, if they exist, are there to be overcome, Mr Bond. I agree with Miss Hill's suggestion in principle, and will make it my business to put forward the case in as persuasive and accurate manner as possible."

Octavia was now beaming. "I'm sure the matter is in excellent hands, Mr Hunter. I am familiar with your work in rescuing so many of our suburban commons from encroachment."

"Thank you. I consider it a privilege to be able to work for such worthy causes."

"Your successes elsewhere will hold us in good stead, and the public must be made aware of these problems." Hunter nodded his assent as she carried on, "the more that other areas are closed off, the more intensely precious these existing open lands become - a place of recreation for the poor and the disenfranchised."

She paused at this, and Hunter took the opportunity to speak again. "Indeed," he said, "and if I might be bold enough to make a suggestion, Miss Hill..."

"Please, Mr Hunter." She tilted her head to show she was paying attention.

"Our Society could well use more members who share your dedication. I was wondering if you and Mr Bond would consider swelling our ranks."

"Well, for my part, I'd be delighted," said Bond immediately.

"Thank you, Mr Hunter," Octavia smiled at him, "I have been involved in the past as you must know, and I do not think you will find me wanting either in ideas or action for the future."

"Then we are birds of a feather, Miss Hill," said Hunter smiling, "and I look forward to helping you bring such ideas to fruition."

Octavia Hill and the Inclosure Act

In 1876 the Disraeli administration presented a Bill 'Facilitating the regulation and improvement of commons, and the amendment of the Inclosure Acts.'

With the backing of the Commons Preservation Society, Octavia Hill published a forthright article attacking the Act. Landowners were taken to task for the way in which they patronised farm labourers and took from them the heritage of their common lands:—

"Should we stand by and let them part with what ought to be a possession to the many in the future? A few coals at Christmas, which come to be looked upon as a charity graciously accorded by the rich, may in many cases be blindly accepted by cottagers in lieu of Common Rights. Do not let us deceive ourselves as to the result if this Bill pass unamended."

The Bill was passed, but the force with which the Society had put forward its case changed the collective attitude of the Inclosure Commissioners and the number of enclosures approved dwindled to a trickle.

'Inval', Haslemere, 1882

The door to the lounge at *Inval* swung open, and Jonathan Hutchinson strode in, his clothes still wet from the rain despite removing his overcoat and gaiters in the hall. Now in his fifty-fourth year, he still worked long hours as a surgeon at the London Hospital. He slept at their London home during the week, but today being Friday, he had caught the evening train from Waterloo to Haslemere as he did most weekends.

Jane looked up from her drawing as he entered, startled by the suddenness of his arrival. "Jonathan," she exclaimed, "you surely did not *walk* from the railway station?"

"My dear wife," he replied, going over to peck her on the cheek, "I have walked considerably further than that in my youth, and enjoyed every minute of it."

"But in this weather?" she retorted.

"It may seem almost perverse to say so," he replied moving to the fire, "but I like the feeling of real nature, even when rough and extremely disagreeable."

"But thou art now a gentleman of over 50 years." She lapsed into her Quaker vernacular. "Thou must..."

"Bless thee woman," her husband cut in. Then, with a chuckle, "I am not ready for my grave yet!"

"Mr Hutchinson..." she protested with mock formality.

"We all try to live too fast these days," he continued. "As a doctor I've seen it. One doing it sets a bad example for others to follow, till we all end up striving for a false and artificial standard."

He was off on one of his hobby-horses again, and Jane was determined to rein him in. "You are here in Haslemere now," she chided him. "You can leave the pressures of London behind for a few days."

Hutchinson sighed as he stretched in front of the blazing logs. "There's the book to be written," he said flatly.

Jane knew which of many learned tomes her husband was currently engaged on. *"Leprosy and Fish Eating* can wait for an hour or two," she said, more cuttingly than she had intended.

He looked at her, and understood it was time to change the subject. "How are the children?" he asked.

"Bernard is feeling better today - at least, better enough to want to go out. Ursula and Agnes are out with him, Herbert is helping with the livestock, and as for the others ..." she paused, searching for words.

"They are really too old to be called children any more," her husband added.

"Elsie is 25 now - I cannot believe it sometimes. It seems like only the other day that we first went to Haslemere market and could hardly understand what the traders were saying."

"Fifteen years ago," he said. "I think we have come to know the people of Haslemere quite a bit better in that time."

"And they us," she added. Then, suddenly remembering, "Oh, by the way, Mr W was round the other day wishing to speak with thee."

"More trouble?"

"Only more of the same I think. He still complains we are spoiling his sport on Stoatley by building houses there."

"Mr W objects to houses on Stoatley because it is such a good partridge ground! There is this desire of the old families about Haslemere to keep the land to themselves." He took the poker and gave a log in the fire a sharp prod amid a flurry of sparks. "It is simply an unconscious selfishness," he said to Jane as he prodded again, "with which I cannot conceive

that thou hast any sympathy."

"They feel it is their birthright."

Hutchinson turned. "It is a great mistake of theirs to think that other people do not enjoy the country, or are not worthy of it."

Octavia Hill in 1877

"They think..." started his wife, but he held up his hand to her and continued, "To think of many other children obtaining the kind of enjoyment and health which theirs have had, and we were pleased to give ours, ought to be a constant source of satisfaction to them."

"I fear they do not see it that way," she said.

But this was not an issue on which her husband was prepared to give ground. "I should on principle," he said, "be prepared to make any sacrifice which would enable a larger number of city residents, for longer periods, to obtain the kind of advantages which we have enjoyed."

"Perhaps," said Jane, "but they..."

"Children are more than partridges, Jane - remember that," he said, adding the epilogue to his sermon.

"Aye, Jonathan." Jane felt the subject had run its course.

He moved to her and looked over her shoulder at the sketch on the table. "Come - shall we eat? And then after, show me what drawings thou hast made since I was last here."

Taking her hand in his, he helped her to rise. "Tomorrow I shall see Mr W myself," he said as they crossed to the dining room, "and then we shall weigh his philosophy against mine."

Epping Forest, 6th May 1882

The great procession had come and gone. Now, amid all the celebratory bunting and flags, the two architects of the success stood together. George Shaw Lefevre grasped Robert Hunter by the hand. "Congratulations, Robert! Without your efforts I doubt that it could have been achieved."

"You give me too much credit, sir," Hunter replied in typically modest fashion. "I was but one small part of the affair."

"You are too self-effacing, man," retorted the other. "This was by far our greatest battle, and it was won largely through your industry. Sixteen lords of the manor involved, barrowloads of documents wheeled in, Lord knows how many hundreds of witnesses summoned..."

"Just seventy," Hunter corrected.

"Over modest, Robert. The whole thing extended over the course of more than three years, and you were a young man for such a complicated legal battle." Then, patting him on the back, he said, "You succeeded, and I can tell you now, Robert, I never had my doubts."

Hunter smiled. "Thank you."

"Not only did you save Epping Forest from enclosure, but today it is declared open as a Public

Park by none other than Her Majesty the Queen."

"You know I thrive on working for causes I can believe in."

Shaw Lefevre nodded sagely - the man did indeed seem to thrive on work. "Mind you," he said, "you were a single man in those days. I doubt if you could manage all the late-night meetings now, a married man with your first daughter. How are they, by the way?"

"Ellen is well, and Dorothy is nearly a year old now," said Hunter with some pride.

"Soon be walking, then there'll be no peace in the house."

Hunter smiled in agreement. Having started a family, and with the prospect of other additions to follow, he and Nellie had recently decided to join the ever-growing band living away from the smoke of the city. "We are considering moving out into the country," he told Lefevre, "somewhere convenient for travelling to London."

Lefevre laughed. "Here by Epping Forest perhaps, now that you have secured its tranquillity?"

Hunter shared the joke, but shook his head. "No, I am attracted to Surrey. My father was sent to Dorking on medical advice some twenty years ago. We moved with him, and I became well acquainted with the commons and hills around there. I still think of the whole area with great affection."

"Then I shall look forward to visiting you." Lefevre spoke the words, but his thoughts were elsewhere. He had started this line of conversation for a reason, and now was the time to broach the subject.

"Robert, there was another matter I wished to raise with you today." Hunter's eyes narrowed with interest as the other went on, "Your work here with the Commons Preservation Society has not gone unnoticed, and I believe you owe it to yourself to consider what other posts might benefit from your keen legal mind."

"Other posts? D'you have anything particular in mind?"

"I have one," replied Lefevre. "Indeed I have been so forward as to mention your name already to the director of a certain body, with a strong recommendation in your favour."

"This body being?"

"The Post Office, Robert. It has become a large and complex enterprise in the forty years or more since the penny post was inaugurated."

Hunter nodded. "A vital organisation," he said, "which we all now take for granted."

"But the future offers much more." Shaw Lefevre spoke with the burning interest of one soon to become Postmaster General himself. "More than just delivering envelopes and packets. Think of telegraph for instance, and the new telephone exchanges in London."

"You think they too will become Post Office functions?"

"I believe they will, in the fullness of time - but not without some legal battles." He paused significantly. "Which is why I recommended *you* to the Postmaster General, Professor Fawcett, for the position of Legal Adviser. Does it interest you?"

"One does not lightly brush aside the opportunity to be active in such important matters."

"Other names have been put forward," warned Lefevre, "but I think you have the edge on them." Then, almost as an afterthought, "We'll miss you here of course, at the Society."

The younger man's reaction was as he had expected. "You know I should still be available to you, to assist where I can."

Shaw Lefevre looked concerned. "I know you're one for hard work, Robert, and you take no money for a large proportion of what you do - but remember, you're a married man now with a growing family."

But Hunter's mind was already busy tackling the likely problems of the new position. "I'm sure I shall be able to find time enough for both work and family," he replied instinctively.

Shaw Lefevre gave him a stern look, and his words were prophetic. "Well we shall see," he said, "but Robert, I shouldn't like to see you beat me to an early grave."

Tyndall's Hut on Hindhead, March 1883

Professor John Tyndall had made his name in two very different fields of endeavour by the time he moved to Hindhead with his wife in 1883. Not only was he an eminent physicist and a Fellow of the Royal Society, but he had also been a renowned Alpine climber in his youth, making one of the earliest assaults on the Matterhorn and the first ascent of the Weisshorn.

The Devil's Punch Bowl, Hindhead, in early 20th C

He was convinced that the air at Hindhead was as pure as that in the Alps, and was determined to build himself a 'retreat for his old age' there. While his house was being constructed, however, he erected a little hut amid what he described as the 'wild and lovely moorland with vast expanses of heather.' Here, he and his wife Louisa stayed, 'making our own tea, cooking our own chops, and boiling our own potatoes,' as he said in a letter to a friend.

They advertised for someone to come in as an occasional tidy woman, and Louisa was now showing a local girl, Mary, what the job would involve.

"You see it's just the one room inside," she said, ushering the girl through the front door.

Mary looked round in amazement. These were London folk - important folk - and here they were living in a small place like this in the middle of nowhere. "Yes, ma'am," was all she could say.

"Very small," Louisa admitted, speaking the girl's thoughts, "and we'd just ask you to wash up and arrange things back in their place. I'm afraid Mr Tyndall and I are not the tidiest of people."

The girl was still trying to take it in. "No, ma'am," she said, then remembering her manners added, "I mean, I'm sure I'll manage, ma'am."

"As far as cooking is concerned, we'll be doing our own on the little range there."

"Will you be wanting me every day?"

"Only when we're here. My husband and I will be in London some of the time, and we also travel to Switzerland each year."

"I see."

"We'll give you good warning of our arrival."

Mary nodded and gave a little smile. She'd been worried that these famous people would frighten her, but now she was feeling braver. "It's very, sort of, lonely out here isn't it?" she said. "Nobody else in sight, I mean."

Louisa laughed. "After the smoke of London it's like heaven, escaping here to this little hut," she said. "The heather is like a purple sea around us, and the air is so fresh." She gave Mary a confiding look. "Mr Tyndall is very happy not to see another person when we stay here, and so am I."

Tyndall's hut at Hindhead in the 1880s

Mary assumed the restriction was not meant to apply to her. "I live down in the village," she said, "I can walk up here when you need me."

"That's good." The sound of boots could be heard approaching outside. "Ah, here's my husband now."

John Tyndall stepped through the door with the chill blast of a March wind behind him. He pulled it to, then noticed they had a visitor. His wife made the introduction, "John, I'd like you to meet Mary - she will tidy for us."

Tyndall saw a plump and slightly anxious young country girl in front of him. He smiled. "My wife's told you I make a mess, has she?"

"Well sir, she's..." Mary was unsure again.

"I liken my working method to the nest-making of the macaw," he continued taking off his hat and cloak. "The male brings in stick after stick, piling them up around the poor female, until the wall becomes too great, then she gets to work to sort the mess out."

His wife decided the poor girl had been teased enough. "I'm sure Mary will cope very well with us," she said. Then to Mary, "Will you start tomorrow?"

"Yes, ma'am."

"We'll see you here in the morning then."

Relieved that the interview was over, Mary bobbed politely and departed for home across the common, wrapping her shawl round her and bending into the wind which had just blown John Tyndall back to the hut.

Louisa looked at her husband with concern. "Are you feeling better for your walk, John?" His health had not been good over the last few years - indeed, it was the very reason they were moving here.

"Wonderful!" he replied. "It's been almost as cold as an alpine glacier out there recently, but I feel so much better for a few days away from London."

"That's a relief," she said with feeling, and went to put the kettle on the range. "I'll make us a pot of tea."

"Thank you." Then, starting to remove his boots he said, "I've just been looking at the site for our house. They're sinking the well."

"How are they doing?" The house was being built nearby on one of the highest points of the common.

"They've just tapped water at 215 feet in the Lower Greensand - soft as dew and clear as crystal."

The mention of holes in the ground prompted her to ask, "Have you had any further correspondence about those Channel tunnel borings at Dover?" Tyndall had recently added his learned thoughts to the public debate raging on the subject.

"I don't think they will come to anything," he said.

Louisa looked up. "I thought you felt it was quite feasible."

"Oh technically it is," he agreed. "It's politics not the engineering which will stop it. Fear of invasion by the French."

His wife's thoughts drifted back to their new house again. "You know," she said, "I shall be sorry, in a way, to leave our little hut for a proper house. I'm very happy here."

"Not the reaction people might expect from the daughter of a Lord and a Lady," said her husband, finally removing his second boot.

Louisa laughed. "My father showed the Queen his bare bottom, remember."

"He was a little younger then, I recall." Tyndall remembered the story well - she had told him many times before - how her grandfather had been honoured to receive a visit from the Queen and her family at his estate in Scotland, and how, to make room, he had turned out his own children from the main house to a smaller one. All were happy with the arrangement except one, Louisa's father-to-be, who showed his displeasure when presented to the Queen by refusing to bow. Instead he stood upside down - a trick he had learnt recently - and affronted the sovereign by showing her he wore nothing under his kilt.

"She was not amused," said Louisa. "It's true what they say about Scotsmen and their undergarments you know." Well-worn as the story had become, it still raised a laugh each time she told it.

"This hut will still be standing in the grounds when the house is built, and we can use it when we wish," said Tyndall replying to his wife's concern.

"Not quite the same though," she replied.

But there was a positive side to the move. "With a house here we can move my library down from London, and we can start on our biography." They had been meaning to start on 'their' biography for many years, but never seemed to get round to it.

"And I can help you become an organised and tidy person!" chided his wife.

"Not much chance of that I'm afraid, my dear Louisa," he replied with a chuckle.

She approached with a full tray. "Here's the tea." Then, seeing the papers and other paraphernalia littered all over their only table, she added with a sigh, "Can we find a space for it, please John?"

Haslemere, July 1883

Threats of enclosure by land owners brought strong reactions from local people, and William Allingham, now living with his wife Helen at Sandhills near Witley, began a petition against one such instance. Arriving at Haslemere station one day, he began looking for people to add their names to his list.

'Aldworth', the Tennysons' house on Blackdown

"Now, sir, have you heard about Lord Derby's plans to enclose his property up towards Hindhead?" The man he addressed stopped, but showed reluctance to become involved with a complete stranger. Allingham persisted, "He only bought it recently, but we're told he's thinking of fencing off some of the open space there."

The man shook his head and moved on. Allingham tried another. "I think you'll agree, won't you sir, there's an awful lot too much of our countryside being taken away from us right now." This time he had better luck - the person had heard of the threat, and Allingham pressed him, "Will you sign our petition against the enclosure?" He did so - one more signature. "That's very kind of you, sir."

A lady looked interested, and he offered the paper to her - "Madam?" - and by way of giving the matter more weight, added, "I've already got Professor Tyndall's signature here - caught him at the station."

In this way he collected several names, while all the time moving through the town towards his intended goal. "Yes, I'm off to get Mr Tennyson's signature now," he assured one well-wisher, as he made his way along the road to *Aldworth*. Arriving somewhat out of breath after the climb, he met Tennyson's elder son at the gate.

"Good day to you, Hallam."

"Hello, Mr Allingham - how are you?"

"I'm well, thank you," he replied, leaning on the gate-post for support and holding the petition in his other hand.

"You have some more poems there?" Allingham and his father often swapped notes on verses they were writing, or more often re-writing.

"Poems?" said Allingham, confused for the moment. "No, it's a petition I have here. Is your father in?"

"He is - just up from his afternoon rest."

Normally this was not a good time of day to visit the great man, now in his seventy-fourth year, but Allingham had forgotten in his keenness to get signatures. Hallam led him into the house and towards his father's study. Tennyson was seated in an armchair beside a table piled high with books.

"Allingham, just the man. Perhaps you can help."

Allingham was familiar with such requests and wondered what it would be about this time. "I'll do my best," he replied.

"I'm not satisfied with this." Tennyson took a volume off the table and started to search through the pages. "Where is it now? - I was reading it earlier - ah yes, here." He opened the book fully and began to recite in his majestic voice, *"Low-flowing breezes are roaming the broad valley dimm'd in the gloaming..."* He read a few stanzas then said to Allingham, "You know the one - what do *you* think of it?"

Strange, thought Allingham to himself, how the greatest living poet of the day should still feel the need to review and criticise his earlier work in this way. "That's a very old favourite of mine," he said. "I hope you won't alter it."

The older man looked at him. "Some of the things in it don't seem to agree with the time spoken of."

"The total effect is harmonious though," protested Allingham. "It's like a landscape in an old Italian picture."

"I know, but I fear the water-gnats are not right - they would not be out so late."

At this Allingham laughed out loud. That such trivialities should trouble the man! He shook his head. "I shouldn't be too concerned with the water-gnats," he said.

Tennyson was not entirely convinced. "I shall put it by for further consideration," he replied, then noticed for the first time the paper in Allingham's hand. Unlike Hallam, he realised at once that it was not poetry. Locally, Allingham was as well-known for his campaigns as for his verse. "You have a letter there," he observed.

"To Lord Derby," said Allingham, "concerning an enclosure he's threatening to make."

"Should I sign?" The Poet Laureate was already holding out his hand for it.

"Your signature would add considerable weight."

"You already have Tyndall I see."

"He told me that he knew Lord Derby intended to keep the beauty of the place unspoilt," Allingham admitted, "but we can never be too sure, can we."

Tennyson's Lane, Blackdown

"Well I'll add my name, for what good it may do." He took a pen from the holder and made his mark. "Now let us talk of other things," he said, and they spent an hour or more in further discussion before the light outside began to fade and Allingham insisted he must go. Tennyson walked out with him onto Blackdown, and pointed to the sky in the west. "Have you noticed the sunsets we're having just now?" he said. They had been a strange, rich colour for some days.

"Volcanic they say," Allingham remarked.

"The floating ghost of a mountain blown to atoms." Tennyson's sonorous voice somehow matched the splendour in the heavens.

They stood watching the red glow, and Allingham was reminded of another, more human glory which Tennyson had recently observed. "How was your steamer trip with Gladstone and the Great Folk?" he asked. "You read them *The Grandmother*, did you not?"

"The Princess of Wales asked for it - she had heard it read before."

"And her sister, the Tsarina?"

Tennyson chuckled. "When I had done, the ladies praised me, and I patted the unknown one on the back by way of reply. Only afterwards did I find out she was the Empress of Russia!"

"And how did the Tsar take it?"

"He looked very stern. I am probably lucky still to be alive."

Allingham started to move on. "I must go down to Mr Hodgson for his signature before it gets too late."

"Then let me accompany you to the Sussex Gate."

"You will not step over into Surrey tonight?"

"No - but I'll strike the gatepost with my stick; I generally do - like Johnson did with the posts in Fleet Street." And with that the two men walked into the gathering dusk, down the lane towards Haslemere.

'Meadfield', Haslemere, October 1883

Robert and Ellen Hunter moved to *Meadfield* in Haslemere soon after he had taken the post of legal adviser to the Post Office. The Postmaster General, Professor Henry Fawcett, was a remarkable man, not least because he had been blinded in a shooting accident at the age of 25, yet still managed to pursue a number of impressive careers during the rest of his life.

'Meadfield', the Hunters' home in Haslemere

He was married to a no less remarkable woman, Dame Millicent Fawcett, née Garrett, who had founded Newnham College some twelve years earlier. The Hunters had invited him and his wife to visit them in their new home. The Allinghams were also invited, but the Fawcetts arrived first.

"Won't you come in?" Ellen guided them into the sitting room.

"Thank you, Mrs Hunter."

"I think over here..." She indicated a sofa by the window, and Dame Millicent escorted her husband towards it.

"I hope we are not too early for you."

Ellen was quick to reassure her. "Not at all."

Professor Fawcett was now seated. "How are you liking your new house?" he asked.

"Very well, thank you professor. A great change from London."

"I certainly smell a difference in the air," he said. "You have a wonderful view from here, I am told."

Ellen checked herself from asking him to admire it. "Across the valley, yes," she said in a somewhat louder voice than was necessary.

Dame Millicent was her husband's eyes. "It's a beautiful part of the world. We are in Surrey here?" she asked.

"Close to the border with Sussex, just over there," Ellen pointed out of the window.

"And with Hampshire too, I believe," added the professor.

"Yes." Ellen was strangely unprepared for such a comment from him. She turned to Dame Millicent in reply, "There is a spot not too distant from here where one may stand on a bridge at the point the three counties meet."

The latter took another look through the window before sitting down next to her husband. "You say you have invited the Allinghams tonight? I have always admired her paintings. She must find a great deal of inspiration living in such attractive surroundings."

"Her husband is a poet, is he not?" asked the professor. "Seems to be quite the place for poets."

Ellen instinctively indicated the window again. "You can almost see Mr Tennyson's house from here..."

Robert entered the room at that moment. "My apologies," he said, "for not greeting you when you arrived." The Fawcetts began to rise. "No, no, please don't get up." He went over to them and shook hands. "How was the journey?"

"Fine until some fool pulled the communication cord just before Haslemere," growled the professor. "We were almost thrown from our seats."

"Was there a good reason?" asked Hunter.

"None that we could see."

"A man was seen running away across the fields," added Dame Millicent. "Quite a respectable looking gentleman."

Ellen Hunter in later years

"Probably taking a short cut home," said the professor. Then, changing the subject abruptly, "Well, Hunter, so this is where you are when you're not at the Post Office."

Robert smiled. "When not attending to your ideas for a parcel post and the implementation of postal orders. And I hear Shaw Lefevre is trying to interest you now in the idea of a sixpenny telegram."

Fawcett gave a sharp laugh. "So he is. We're keeping you busy."

Ellen answered for her husband, "Busy enough to be away from home most of the week." A look of irritation flashed across Hunter's brow, but she appeared unaware of it, asking him, "Have the Allinghams arrived yet?"

"Yes my dear, they are just removing their boots. They have walked over from Sandhills," he added to the Fawcetts.

"I was saying to your wife how much I enjoy looking at Helen Allingham's work," said Dame Millicent.

"A talented lady," Hunter agreed. "She is very friendly with Mrs Hutchinson - you know, the wife of the eminent surgeon. They have a house in the next valley."

"Ah, Dr Jonathan Hutchinson - yes." This seemed to set off a spark in Dame Millicent, and she spoke his name with feeling. "What was it he said about my sister?"

"Your sister?" said Ellen uncertainly.

"My wife's sister Elizabeth," explained the professor, "became the first woman doctor in England."

"Elizabeth Anderson," added his wife. "When she was appointed, Mr Hutchinson was quoted as saying, 'I am sorry for the decision - it is too absurd.'"

"Mind you," the professor confided to Hunter, "I'm told that once when she was engaged to attend a lady, they ran so close a race it seemed likely they might both be confined on the same day."

The men began to chuckle together at this, which did not please Dame Millicent. "A typical male reaction, don't you think," she said pointedly to Ellen.

The situation was defused by the entry of the Allinghams themselves. Hunter moved swiftly to meet them and made the formal introductions, then

Ellen and Dame Millicent took Helen Allingham to one side leaving the men to converse on their own.

"By your voice I gather you are from Ireland, Mr Allingham," said Fawcett.

"County Donegal," Allingham confirmed.

"And currently working on a collection of Irish songs and poems, I believe," said Hunter.

"When I'm not chasing all over the country for signatures."

Sir Robert Hunter in 1907

Hunter explained to Fawcett, "Mr Allingham is a tireless campaigner against local enclosures here."

"Good man," declared Fawcett.

"Did you catch Tennyson?" asked Hunter.

"I did too - on my feet all the way up to *Aldworth*, and then back down to get Hodgson at Lythe Hill."

"We shall need to keep a close watch if we're to stop

the commons here being parcelled up before our eyes," Hunter said.

At that moment the gong sounded for dinner, and Ellen returned to them. "May I escort you into dinner, professor?" she asked.

"With great pleasure, my dear Mrs Hunter."

Robert Hunter took the arm of Helen Allingham, and William was left to offer his to Dame Millicent. "May I have the honour?" he asked.

"It appears you have Hobson's choice, Mr Allingham," she said with good humour.

"And I'm delighted at that, madam," he replied as they followed the others out of the room.

A Room in London, 1883

Robert Hunter had left the Commons Preservation Society, and Percival Birkett had replaced him as Honorary Solicitor. However, this did not stop Hunter from offering his services whenever they were needed over the years.

Hardwicke Rawnsley was in London today. He was a tireless and fiery campaigner for the preservation of the countryside, particularly in his adopted Lake District, and had fought off a number of previous plans for reservoirs and railways in the region, but now he had come to ask for the Society's help in averting one more menace.

"Yet another wretched railway bill," he said to Birkett when they met, "this time along the lakeside at Windermere."

"You defeated the Derwentwater and Borrowdale proposals Mr Rawnsley, let us hope you achieve the same result again."

"Hope is not enough," said Rawnsley with emotion. "There was such passionate local opposition last time that the speculators were forced to withdraw - but this time, can we be sure?"

"Mr Hunter guaranteed you money to fight on the previous occasion, did he not?"

"Most generously, but I fear money alone will not be sufficient at Windermere. What we need here is his skilled legal brain."

Stewart Hodgson

"You understand, he now works for the Post Office, but I know how much he sympathises with your cause. I have asked him if he can be present today."

"I gather he still holds considerable influence here in the Society."

"Frankly, I don't know where he finds the time, but hardly a week has gone by without him giving me assistance in one way or another since I took over."

"A talented and indefatigable man."

"Indeed, seemingly inexhaustible," nodded Birkett, "and also a good friend."

At that, Hunter appeared through the door, almost on cue, carrying a folder bulging with papers.

"Percival, I am sorry to have kept you waiting - Mr Rawnsley, we meet again - how are you?"

"Very well in myself, thank you Mr Hunter, but concerned as ever about my lakes. The way the railway companies move..."

"Well, we shall see what we can do about that," Hunter cut in. "I have taken the opportunity to study the details of the Bill..."

"Already?"

"... and I believe, there are some parts of it which might lend themselves to a successful appeal."

Birkett smiled. "That's encouraging news, Robert."

"If we may move to a larger table, Percival, I'll explain the sections which I feel are best open to attack."

"We can spread out through here, in the office," said Birkett turning to lead the way. Rawnsley held Robert back for a moment. "You have lifted my spirits already, Mr Hunter."

"There is still much work to be done as I am sure you appreciate, Mr Rawnsley, but yes, I think we should be able to bring about a satisfactory result. Shall we spend a few minutes considering our approach together?" And with that, the two men followed Birkett into the office.

Lythe Hill House, Haslemere, August 1884

Mrs Hodgson and Mrs Hunter had been hard at work all day preparing for an 'at home' evening at *Lythe Hill*. It was a weekday, and their husbands were both in London for the night - a not infrequent occurrence, as there were no trains out of Waterloo after about seven o'clock. Now the guests had arrived and things were in full swing.

The hostess managed to catch up with her friend again during a brief lull in the proceedings. "My dear Mrs Hunter, it was so good of you to come and help me organise this."

"It was nothing. With both of our husbands away on business it seemed the most obvious thing to do. We women should not let our men steal all the limelight."

"I know you have strong views on the matter," said Mrs Hodgson. Then after a pause she added, "Your husband is still working on behalf of the Commons Preservation Society, is he not?"

Ellen Hunter gave a short laugh. "Yes," she said. "He has a busy enough job with the Post Office, yet he still manages to find time to do a great deal of detailed work for the Society. At the moment they are trying to save a building in Deptford."

"Ah yes, Sayes Court, Mr Evelyn's house. I have read about it. Did it not have associations with the Tsar of Russia at one time?"

Lythe Hill House, the Hodgsons' home in 1884

"I gather one of the Tsars and his party rather wrecked the place many years ago, when he was over here to study shipbuilding, but it is now some sort of Museum."

"And threatened with demolition if no purchaser is found I believe?"

"Mr Evelyn is an old, and I suspect eccentric man,"

said Mrs Hunter. "He wishes to donate the house and grounds to the public, but there appears to be no organisation available to accept it. My husband is studying the legal situation to see if some such public company can be formed quickly, but he fears it will be in vain."

"That seems a shame," said Mrs Hodgson, but she held no very strong views on this particular issue and it came out sounding a little trite. Ellen decided it was time to change the subject.

"Well, the evening has gone well so far, has it not?" she volunteered. "Lord Tennyson is at his best - his new peerage seems to sit well on him."

"And Hallam's new wife is charming, don't you think?" agreed Mrs Hodgson.

At this moment Helen Allingham entered the room alone, and Ellen turned to her with a smile. "Ah, Mrs Allingham, has your husband left you unattended?"

"He has. He and Mr - I mean Lord - Tennyson are deep in conversation about Irish dialects." She was having difficulty, as they all were, in remembering that they now had a peer in their midst.

"Did I not see you at Valewood House the other day," said Mrs Hodgson, "painting in Mr Mangles' grounds?"

"You may well have done," said Helen, "I often stay there as a friend of the family. The rhododendrons have finished now of course, but there are some charming cottages to study, and I am also doing a few portraits for them."

At this, Mrs Hodgson insisted the two ladies should come with her to another room and view some paintings her husband had recently acquired. As they moved out, Tennyson and Allingham walked in, discussing poetry as ever.

"Are you determined to write this Irish poem in brogue?" Allingham asked.

"Do you disapprove?"

"I consider you'll offend the Irish by doing it."

"It's based on a report I read recently about a body dug out of the peat which was so well preserved you could identify every detail."

William Allingham in 1884

Allingham was not impressed. "It happens all the time over there," he said.

"But you're from the North," continued Tennyson, "and this is set in the South - you'll have the wrong accent for me."

"I know various Irish brogues - have you chosen any one in particular?"

Tennyson produced a manuscript from one of his copious pockets. "It's called *Tomorrow*," he said.

Allingham looked at it for a while, then laughed out loud. "That's fine," he said, "that's great. I see. You've started it with the girl saying 'tomorra' - meaning 'top o the morning' - and then given it the title *Tomorrow*. Very good, I like that." He read on. "But you'll have to strike the 'h' out of McGhee - they don't spell it that way."

Tennyson appeared grateful for the advice. "Will you spend some time on this with me up at *Aldworth*?" he asked.

"I'd be delighted," replied Allingham. "And can we go again to that little summer house you've just built at the end of Blackdown, to see the wide vista of the Sussex weald spread out before us?"

In reply, the new Lord quoted a stanza from a poem he had written for General Hamley,
> *"You came, and look'd and loved the view*
> *Long-known and loved by me.*
> *Green Sussex fading into blue*
> *With one grey glimpse of sea."*

"And in the far, occasional distance, due east," added Allingham, "that elusive church spire of - well, we're not quite sure where, are we?"

"You said you thought it might be Horsham."

"Near the birthplace of Shelley, I remember," said Allingham.

At this, the ladies returned to the room. "Ah, Lord Tennyson," said Mrs Hodgson going to him, "we must go and join your wife and talk some more with your new daughter-in-law. You must be very proud of her."

"Indeed I am," he replied, and with a bow to the others, he allowed himself to be escorted away by his hostess.

Helen went to her husband. "Mrs Hunter has kindly offered us a lift to the station, William," she said.

"That's very civil of you."

"My pleasure," replied Ellen, "but before we go, I gather there is a performer about to start in the other room - one Corney Grain I believe."

"A comic turn?"

"Hopefully," she laughed, "with a name like that."

View from Blackdown over the Sussex Weald - "Green Sussex fading into blue"

Swan Inn, Haslemere, 16th December 1884

Stewart Hodgson waited for the audience to settle down a little before he checked with the secretary, Ernest Hepburn, and called for order.

"Well ladies and gentlemen," he said when he could finally be heard, "first of all I'd like to thank you for coming here tonight and showing such an interest in what, I believe, we all feel is a cause of vital importance to both Haslemere and the surrounding district. The immediate issue, as I'm sure you are all aware, concerns the recent enclosure of about 30 acres of Hindhead Common at the top of Farnham Lane by the lord of the manor. Now we intend to challenge this enclosure in the name of the commoners who claim to have rights there, but we feel the challenge will be far more effective if carried by a properly formed organisation rather than by individuals. Therefore we have proposed the formation of a Haslemere Committee of the Commons Preservation Society and called this meeting to elect a committee and agree its terms of reference."

A hand went up in the audience. "Mr Chairman, may I ask exactly where this enclosure is?"

Ernest Hepburn answered, "As you go up Farnham Lane, it is the first piece of open land you come to on the left."

"Part, of course," added Hodgson, "of the far larger common stretching up to the gibbet and beyond."

Another hand went up. "Excuse my ignorance, Mr Chairman, but who is the lord of the manor there?"

"It is in the Manor of Frydinghurst," said Hodgson, "and the lord there is General Bishop."

"And what is his reaction so far to this challenge?"

"I think it is best described as 'unsatisfactory,'" replied Hodgson, "hence the need for this meeting."

"I wonder," asked another in the audience, "could you tell us what commoners' rights are, exactly?"

Hepburn had the answer. "Freehold tenants of the manor are entitled to common rights of pasture, of turbary, and of estovers..."

"Of *what*?" said a voice, to general laughter.

"*Turbary*," said Hepburn, "is the taking of turf or peat, and *estovers* are the necessities of life such as the taking of wood for household use or the making of implements."

"Thank you!"

Hepburn continued, "And we also wish to restrain the lord of the manor from enclosing or digging gravel to the injury of the tenants' rights."

Swan Inn, Haslemere, in 1885

Another hand went up. "Which commoners have rights over this piece of land?"

"There are a number of them," replied Hodgson, "but we intend to press the claim in the name of just one - Dr Jonathan Hutchinson, the London surgeon, who is a tenant on part of the property and is, as I am sure you are all aware, a well-known and respected man in many influential circles of society." There was general assent from the audience. "We feel that this will give us the best chance of success."

"And I might add," said Hepburn, "that Dr Hutchinson is very agreeable to this."

Hodgson looked for further questioners, but could see none, so he continued, "The object of our Society, in a nutshell, is to 'preserve the commons and wasteland in the neighbourhood of Haslemere in their open condition.'"

At this, William Allingham rose. "Mr Chairman, may I express a hope that *wayside spaces and footpaths*, as well as commons, will receive full attention from the Preservation Committee. I venture to think that these are particularly interesting to the general public, and likewise very tempting to the private absorbers of public rights. People who are otherwise fair and conscientious in their dealings seems to have little scruple for stealing them."

Hodgson had sympathy for the view, but felt privately that the new Society should not try to run before it could walk. "It would, I am sure, be our intention to include footpaths in our remit at some time in the future, but for the present we are intending to concentrate on the enclosure of open commons."

"Footpaths belong to future generations as well as to ourselves," Allingham insisted.

Hodgson did not want this first meeting to get bogged down in detail. "I believe we should refer that matter to the first committee when it is formed," he said. "We have a number of gentlemen prepared to stand on the executive committee, including Mr Robert Hunter, who most of you know has been active in campaigns fought by the national Commons Preservation Society." There was a murmur of approval. "He has now many famous victories to his credit." To Hunter, sitting in the audience, he said, "I shall not spare your blushes, sir."

Hepburn whispered in Hodgson's ear, and the other nodded. "May I ask the gentlemen who will form

"There was nothing either of us could do," he repeated, "we must not blame ourselves."

Jane turned back to look at her canvas. "Since then I have found little joy in my painting," she said, "or in anything else."

"You have nine other fine children who all look to you for strength and example," he reminded her.

"I know," said Jane with a small smile, "and I thank God for that, believe me I do - but even so I cannot help..." and she struggled to stop the tears flowing again.

Hutchinson believed that positive thinking was the only solution. "I have a mind to walk over Hindhead to see what progress has been made at *Trimmers Wood*. Will you come with me?" he asked.

Jane had never been entirely convinced that her husband's building projects were justified. "Your relaxation appears to be in buying up other people's land and peppering it with houses," she said.

Her husband felt a slight irritation at this, despite her obvious grief. "You know my opinion on that matter well enough," he replied sharply.

It was a recurring point of disagreement between them, and Jane was on familiar ground as she put her argument. "You wish to open up the countryside to all comers, yes. But you cannot deny that such speculation also makes you money at the expense of other people."

Hutchinson knew there was no answer he could make that would satisfy her at the moment. "Come, this is not a time to be quarrelling," he said soothingly. "You are not feeling yourself. A walk will do us both good."

"No." She could not face the prospect of a long climb and the sight of yet another set of half-built walls. "You go - I have promised to help Agnes and Ursula with their needlework." With this, she began to pack up the easel.

"I shall be concerned to leave you here in such low spirits."

Jane forced a thin smile at this. "Go, Jonathan," she said, "I shall be all right. As you say, I have nine other children to sustain me."

He helped her to put away the unused brushes and paints. "I do not simply build to make money, you know."

"I *do* know, husband. Thy thoughts are always for others." She held his arm and looked him in the eyes. "But nevertheless, this is the fourth house we have lived in since we moved to Haslemere. *Trimmers Wood* will be the fifth when it is finished. It would be nice to feel settled some time."

Her husband could never really understand her opposition to moving. "I should have thought that planning and building and furnishing in good taste would have been an attractive occupation for an energetic lady."

Jane sighed. "Not so energetic as I used to be," she told him. But she loved the man, and inevitably his wishes became hers. "Go now and see to your building. Supper will be at the usual time, and then you must get ready to travel to London in the morning."

He gave her a peck on the cheek. One of his objectives in life had always been 'To be happy, and make others happy', but at times like this it was a very difficult creed to follow. He began up the track towards Hindhead, but in a sombre and preoccupied mood.

Hind Head House, March 1887

The Tyndalls had now settled into *Hind Head House*, as they called their new home, and Frederick Pollock had moved to the area at about the same time. He built *Hindhead Court* a mile or so away down the Portsmouth Road. Tyndall knew the family well - he remembered that it was Pollock's mother who had given him a letter of introduction to Tennyson some thirty years ago - and he welcomed the younger man to his house as a friend.

The Tyndalls' new Hind Head House

"So, Frederick, you are not afraid to become a heathen?"

"A heathen, Professor Tyndall?"

The Tyndalls had gained a reputation among the local population for being a little unconventional in their lifestyle. "Certain wicked people around here have spread the report that 'a colony of heathens' is being established by me at Hindhead."

Pollock laughed. "I assume by that they mean intellectuals."

"I told Huxley he should come and join us in our nest some day to complete the evidence," said Tyndall with a grin, "even if only for a little while."

"How long have you been here now?" asked Pollock. He knew they were here before he had arrived.

"Four years since we set up the hut - just over two since the house was built. We had our first Christmas here in '84."

"And yours was the only house up here when I moved in," Pollock recalled, remembering the sight of the solitary building just off the road down to Haslemere.

Tyndall scowled. "No need to remind me of that. Now I'm having to stop every emigrant Londoner from building too close to me. Had to borrow £100 last year, just to buy up land around me to secure some privacy."

"They're only following your good example - there's flattery in imitation."

"I'm not a difficult man to get on with. I allow the public free access to those parts of my property which don't interfere with me and my work" - here the professor looked out of his window - "but I can't stand the noise and the nuisance of seeing buildings go up before my eyes when I'm sitting at my own desk in my own study."

Pollock could sympathise up to a point, but he felt that Tyndall was perhaps making a meal of it - and there were other times when he had certainly not proved easy to get on with. "You've had your difficulties with the Royal Institution", he observed.

Tyndall glanced at him. "They've finally accepted my resignation, did you know that?"

"I did not," the other replied, "but I'm hardly surprised after your running battle with them for so long."

Some years ago, he had been asked to look at a new gas system designed to illuminate lighthouses, invented by a John Wigham of Dublin. He had reported favourably on it, but then found that Wigham's ideas were not being given due credit by the authorities. This had led him to break ranks on a point of principle with several friends in the Institution. "I cannot abide seeing injustices done, Frederick, you know that."

Louisa Tyndall entered the room then. Excusing herself to the visitor, she said to her husband, "It's time to take your medicine, John - Dr Winstanley said you should not miss a dose."

John Tyndall in his study at Hind Head House

Tyndall was not a well man these days, and among other things suffered from gout in his left leg. "What would I do without her, Frederick?" he said holding out his hand to Louisa. "She's my nurse, my scribe, my clerk, my constant companion..."

"Your *wife*," concluded Louisa. Then moving to a side table she poured out a spoonful of medicine from one of the two bottles there. "Here," she said, putting the spoon in his mouth. Tyndall grimaced.

"From your face, it is not a pleasant dose," remarked Pollock.

"Can't do you any good unless it tastes bad, I always say," replied the patient.

Mrs Tyndall replaced the bottle on the table. "Have you any letters for me to write?" she asked him.

"None that can't wait until tomorrow." Then he remembered, "I need to reply to Hirst. Oh, and there's the speech to do..."

"Scientific or political?" asked Pollock.

"Against Gladstone and the Home Rule Bill for Ireland."

Pollock gave a little chuckle. "I might have guessed. You share the Queen's dislike of him."

"Mind you," continued Tyndall, "if the meeting's anything like the one at Haslemere last December, I'll be wasting my breath."

"I heard the disturbances there were organised."

"Certainly nobody heard the speeches."

Mrs Tyndall saw that she was not needed at the moment, and made to leave the room. "I'll come back later to help you write the speech," she said, then over her shoulder added, "you ought to reply to Williamson about your work on the pentane Gas Standard too."

Tyndall sometimes wondered what he would do without her. "You're right," he agreed with a sigh, "I ought," and his eyes were moist as he watched her go.

Pollock gave a small cough. "I mustn't take up any more of your time - you're a busy man." He rose to take leave himself. Wishing to end on a harmonious note, he said, "Will you be going to Bel Alp for the summer?"

"As ever," said Tyndall automatically.

"Then you'll miss the Golden Jubilee celebrations."

Tyndall looked up from his chair. He was 67 years of age and felt that he did not need to do things any longer just because they were expected of him by others. "I hope you won't think me unduly unpatriotic, Frederick," he said with his Irish accent perhaps a little more noticeable than usual, "but I wouldn't miss my summer in the Alps even for the prospect of being squashed by ecstatic crowds in Westminster or roasted by a celebratory bonfire on Hindhead."

Although he did not share all the old man's views, Pollock had a soft spot for him, and found himself smiling as he walked the mile home.

Sandhills, near Witley, 21st June 1887

The Golden Jubilee celebrations in London were a grand affair, and the Allinghams had been fortunate enough to view the parade from a window in Whitehall. They had arrived back home in Sandhills a few hours ago after catching an afternoon train from Waterloo.

William was sitting in an easy chair while Helen checked some of her sketches. "Am I getting old?" he asked. "I'm still feeling exhausted from standing all day long. What time did we get back?"

She looked up and smiled. He was nearly twenty-five years her senior, and it seemed to show more often now. "About half past five," she replied.

"That long" - he looked at his watch. "Four and a half hours. They'll be lighting the bonfires soon - it's getting dark."

"But you wouldn't have missed it in London, would you William?" She started to put her work away in the fading light. "We may never see pageantry like that again as long as we live."

"Missed it? No," said her husband. "Anyway we could hardly refuse when Lord Wolseley offered us his War Office window to watch from, could we?"

"The best view in town, I should think," she agreed.

"The Tennysons were in the Abbey. I wonder if they saw half as much as we did?"

Helen closed her eyes and recalled the scenes. "Forty-four carriages full of Kings, Queens, Princes, Princesses and Maharajahs from all over the world." She knew, because she had counted them. "The procession seemed to go on for ever."

Hardwicke Rawnsley, circa 1900

"And you noticed the banner across the street?" laughed William. "'Good Sovereign, No Change required.' I think the Prince of Wales looked the other way when he saw that." It was well known that the prince couldn't wait to get on the throne, but Victoria steadfastly refused to abdicate in his favour.

"Was that the Prussian Prince riding beside him?" Helen asked.

"With the eagle on his helmet - yes, that was Crown Prince Fritz. He has the same problem as our Bertie, with an indestructible old father still alive and well, and keeping him off the throne."

His wife was gazing out of the window. "Oh look!" she cried, "I think I see a light on Hindhead." Their house was on a ridge and had magnificent views of the surrounding countryside.

William looked himself, and could see nothing for a moment. Then suddenly there was no doubt, as a pillar of flame could be seen in the gathering dusk. "Yes, there it goes, look. That's impressive even from three miles away."

"It caught very quickly," she added.

He pointed to the left, "And another over there on Blackdown, see."

"But much smaller."

"It's further away."

Helen looked back to Hindhead. "I hope they've taken some water up there - it's very dry just now, and that fire must be enormous." Suddenly the flames increased again. "Look at it going!" she exclaimed.

"It's certainly a big one."

"And spreading already, isn't it?" She sounded concerned.

"Difficult to say from here, but they'll have a devil of a job putting it out if it is."

"See," said Helen pointing, "little fires all over the place now - right across the Weald."

Fires were to be lit all across the country at ten o'clock that night. "They should have one here in Witley by now," said William, "shall we go down to it?"

"I thought you were too tired."

"I was," he said, reaching for his jacket, "but seeing the whole country's still celebrating - we'd be dull not to join in, wouldn't we?"

Inside the 'Happy Eater' at Hindhead

Andy came out of his daydream and realised that his coffee was cold. He looked at the other two. "Another coffee, Tony?" he asked. "You Chris?"

"Might as well," said Tony, "then I'll join the queue at the lights to get down to Witley."

Chris was never one to refuse a free drink, even coffee. "Yes, if you're offering," he said.

Andy waved to Miranda. "Three more coffees, please love." She gave him another withering look and went off to get them. While in his trance-like state, he had been thinking of all the bonfires that had been lit on Hindhead in the past to celebrate great events. "What was the last fire they had on Gibbet Hill?" he asked suddenly.

Tony looked at him sideways. "You mean *intentional* fire?" he said.

"I mean *bonfire*, yes," said Andy.

"In '77 wasn't it?" said Chris. "Silver Jubilee."

"No, it was in '88," Tony corrected him, "four hundred years after the Spanish Armada."

Chris remembered. "That's right."

"I suppose the next one will be at the turn of the century," mused Andy. "The millennium."

"Unless there's anything to celebrate before then," said Chris.

Tony laughed and looked out of the window. "Like a road tunnel under Hindhead you mean?"

"I said *before* the turn of the century!" said Chris dryly.

Miranda arrived with the coffees. "Three coffees," she announced. "That's two pounds ninety-seven."

Andy reached in his pocket for a five pound note....

Hindhead Common, 21st June 1887

Walking back home from the bonfire on Hindhead, Stewart Hodgson with his wife and a friend passed a stall which had been set up that evening to serve hot soup. There was a chill in the air now, and he stopped to buy them a mugful each.

"Three hot soups? That will be ninepence please," said Mrs White, a large lady wielding a large ladle.

Hodgson reached in his pocket for a shilling piece....

"What did you think of the fire, Mr Hodgson?" she asked. Being the largest land-owner in the area, there were very few who did not recognise him.

"Magnificent, didn't you think?" he replied. "All credit to the organisers. Fifteen waggon loads of timber they used, I'm told, and all safely fired and burnt."

Rawnsley's Jubilee Bonfires

In 1887, the stress of fighting the landowners over rights of way plus his parish work was making Rawnsley ill. He spent the early part of the year travelling in Europe on an extended period of leave.

No sooner was he back in Keswick, however, than he was caught up once again in a maelstrom of activity. He was asked to co-ordinate the organisation of great bonfires which were to burn on beacons and mountain tops throughout the kingdom in celebration of Queen Victoria's Golden Jubilee.

Since the days of the Armada, national triumphs had been celebrated in this way, and in Wordsworth's time bonfires were lit nationwide to mark the victory at Waterloo. The preparations completely absorbed him, and he could scarcely have been unaware of their significance at a period when many old beacon sites had been fenced off and barred to the public.

Mrs Hodgson took a sip of the steaming liquid. "This really is delightful soup, Mrs White," she said.

"I thought you'd like something to warm you on your way home."

"A wonderful way to end the evening," she replied. "I'm sure everyone will remember the Golden Jubilee on Hindhead for a very long time to come."

"Most of Haslemere seemed to be here," remarked her husband, looking about him. "I didn't see Hutchinson though, did you?"

"No," she replied, "but then with Jane being so poorly..."

'Inval', Haslemere, September 1887

Jane Hutchinson passed away without seeing her first grandchild born. Ethel had married Allen Chandler in January of that year, but in August her mother was laid to rest in Haslemere churchyard next to young Bernard.

A month later, the pair visited Ethel's father at *Inval*, and were sitting in the lounge waiting for supper. "All things considered I think he's coping remarkable well," said Allen.

Ethel smiled thinly. "She always felt *he* would be the first to go - but I think she never really got over Bernard's death."

"And with our baby due in two months time - she would have enjoyed that."

"Father will enjoy it doubly to make up, I'm sure," Ethel replied more brightly. "You know how he is with children - he adores them."

"Which brings us to the question of the influx," said Allen sombrely.

Ethel looked at her husband. "You can't blame him, Allen. He loves to help other people, and with mama gone he feels it all the more."

"Has he written to them yet?"

She shook her head. "No, it's just an idea at the moment, but he will - I know him. He feels responsible for them." Her father had announced plans to invite his widowed sister and sister-in-law to live at *Inval* together with their families.

"But they have ten young children between them," protested Allen. "I know the house here is large, but..."

Ethel broke in, "Oh, it will be fun! Can't you imagine? The place will come back to life again - just as it was when *I* was a child. There were ten of *us* then." She realised he had not experienced it. "Think of it," she told him, "boating on the pond, writing up holiday books again..."

Her brother Roger came into the room to catch this last statement. "Who's talking about holiday books?" he asked.

"You remember them, Roger," she said with enthusiasm, "when we were small. I was telling Allen what wonderful times we all had here then."

Roger, now 21, was five years her junior. He nodded. "Out camping in all weathers - you recall that? Up at Coombeswell and all around."

Ethel frowned at him. "You boys did. We young ladies stayed nearer to home."

"We were talking about your two aunts and their families moving in," said Allen.

"It will be so good for their children - and for ours too, of course," she added to Allen.

Allen winked. "You mean our young Allen will be born with a whole set of cousins ready to play with?"

"Oh, you've decided it's going to be a boy, then, and named after yourself," she said, teasing him.

"Family tradition among the Chandlers," he replied.

Ethel turned to her brother, now a medical student. "What do you think, Dr Hutchinson? Will it be a boy?" He laughed. "I don't think there's any way to determine that yet," he said. "You'll just have to wait and see."

"It will be," Allen insisted.

"Well two months from now we'll all know," she replied, patting the bulge in her stomach.

Scene at 'Inval'

There was more laughter, and Jonathan Hutchinson entered the room at that moment looking pleased to hear it. He was not yet 60 years old and, despite his recent bereavement, seemed remarkably sprightly and bright eyed. "Ah, papa - there you are," said Ethel.

"Good evening, sir," added Allen, "I hope you are well."

"Thank you, Allen - I am, and bursting with new ideas."

"The book is completed?" Allen knew his father-in-law had been preparing to publish some more medical research.

"The work on syphilis, yes - with the publishers."

Ethel looked at her husband. "One has to take care sometimes, if asked what field one's father is working in," she said with mock seriousness.

Hutchinson smiled. "There should be no boundaries to the physician's concern for human well-being," and turning to his son he added, "eh Roger?"

"So I'm learning, father," replied Roger with a grin.

"And these new ideas that you're bursting with?" asked Allen.

"A museum, for one," said Hutchinson with purpose. "The creation of a proper *educational* museum."

Allen looked puzzled. "How will it differ from any other?"

Hutchinson had thought about this over many years. "It must be made useful as a means of popular instruction," he said. "A collection of objects of all kinds to interest the ordinary observer."

"A *local* museum, I assume," replied Allen, "with a collection of local objects."

"Certainly not!" the other said fiercely. "Something quite different and of far larger scope." He looked at each of them. "Geology, for example, must be illustrated by fossils from all strata, and Botany, Zoology, and History by specimens from all parts of the world."

"It sounds an enormous undertaking," Roger remarked.

His father became philosophical. "Even the longest journey starts with a single step," he said. "I've already begun to gather some things of interest in the barn here at *Inval*, and now I want to broaden the collection."

"And your young nephews and nieces will enjoy helping you," added Ethel.

Hutchinson looked at her and smiled. "I had thought of that as well."

"I'm glad," she said - then more softly, "it will enable you to take your mind off poor mama's death."

Jonathan Hutchinson, circa 1880

Her father was thoughtful for a moment, then looking at his daughter said, "I cannot think that she is in any melancholy sense 'dead.' She sleeps but her spirit lives."

Allen Chandler cleared his throat. "I'm sure that's true, sir."

"You know," continued Hutchinson pensively, "I used to believe in a Heaven and a Hell - but my mind was changed quite suddenly one day some

years ago, when my first child - that was Elsie, your sister Ethel - was just able to walk." He paused, then speaking to Allen continued, "I was in earnest discussion with a man, when he looked at her and said, 'Can you really believe in a creed which might condemn that child of yours to endless torment, whatever she may do in life? Be honest with yourself - if you believed that, you would never be happy again.' And I have taken that to heart ever since," he concluded.

Three pairs of eyes were fixed on him. His daughter was the first to break the silence. "Dear papa," she said, holding his arm gently. But Hutchinson would not let the maudlin mood continue. "I think it is time we should be thinking about supper," he announced loudly. Then to Allen, "Are we to have the company of that wretched spaniel of yours at table again, Mr Chandler?"

Ethel let his arm drop with a squeal of outrage. "Papa!" she cried.

But Allen was thankful the mood had been lightened. "He's very well trained - we give him the freedom of our own house."

"Well, I've no objection so long as it's your food he shares and not mine," said Hutchinson with a twinkle in his eye. "By the way, are you a Latin scholar?"

Allen Chandler was a lawyer. "I have a smattering, as befits my legal occupation," he replied.

"Then you'll know why our medical Latin is called dog-Latin."

Ethel had experienced her father's sense of humour many times before, and could see what was coming. "Have a care, Allen," she warned her husband, "I fear we are in for one of papa's awful puns."

"I think I've heard this one before as well", said Roger.

Allen pondered the question for a while, then admitted, "I confess I have no idea."

Hutchinson allowed a dramatic pause, then with straight face explained, "Because we use a shortened form, you see, so it's *cur*-tailed!"

Ethel and Roger both winced, while Allen gave the small smile of a man unfairly beaten. "Thank you father," said his daughter with stern good humour. "*Now* shall we prepare for supper?"

A Room in London, November 1889

Robert Hunter continued his involvement with the Commons Preservation Society, trying to form some organisation better equipped to deal with the new pressures on land and property. There had, however, been a frustrating period of several years during which nothing seemed to have happened.

Hunter was by nature a modest and restrained man, but his colleagues in this venture, Octavia Hill and Hardwicke Rawnsley, were more outgoing and emotional in character. At a meeting with Hunter, Octavia voiced her concerns.

"Do you not share my frustration Mr Hunter?

"I find that patient debate, however tiresome, will often win the day, Miss Hill," he replied evenly. "But your concern is..."

"I have already stated my concern," she burst out. "I fear that Mr Shaw Lefevre does not rise to the idea of the new society."

"He errs on the side of caution perhaps, "Hunter admitted.

"It is nearly five years since we raised the notion of a National Trust - five years! - and in that time not one positive move has been made."

Hunter had heard this complaint from her before. He knew that not everybody shared his belief in a slow but steady building up of ideas. "The mills of progress sometimes grind slowly," he remarked.

Octavia brushed his comment aside. "First there

was the meeting at Mr Bryce's house, when he was chairman, and we tried to establish a company by opening a share list at £1 a share."

"Several meetings as I recall," added Hunter.

"Quite. Then Mr Shaw Lefevre resumed the chair, and since then, nothing."

"I feel that is not altogether fair, Miss Hill." Hunter always looked for a positive side to any argument. "You yourself have achieved a measure of success in the Society - with your pressure to include footpaths for instance."

"Hardly success, Mr Hunter," she said tartly, "notoriety perhaps. They are being snatched from us monthly, but it remains the hardest of all things to get either workers or money for their preservation."

Hunter nodded. "I remember poor Allingham making a very similar point in a meeting at Haslemere some years ago - he died just the other day you know."

William Allingham had become ill following a riding accident near Sandhills the previous year. The family had moved back to London, but his health had deteriorated, and Helen became a widow at the age of 40 with a family of three young children to support by her own means. Octavia was on friendly terms with her. "I heard," she said, "and sent my condolences to his wife."

Hunter paused for a while out of respect, then returning to the subject of footpaths said, "Your description of *'the winding ways that lead us on by hedgerows and over brooks, through scented meadows and up grassy hill, away from dusty roads and into the silent green of wood and field'* - do I have it right?..."

"You do," replied Octavia, "I am flattered at your recollection."

"It paints a picture in the mind which I am sure will live on in future generations."

Octavia was not mollified by flattery, however well deserved. "If there are still paths for them to tread," she said. "I feel we are the few unknown heroes fighting an uphill battle for a great cause."

"Which with perseverance we shall win," he replied.

She had just turned 50 and he was in his mid-forties. Neither was getting any younger, and there was still so much to do. "None works harder or with more dedication than yourself Mr Hunter," she said, "but how are we to progress against this brick wall of indifference and obstinacy?"

Hunter's answer was typical of the man, but did nothing to relieve Octavia's immediate anxiety. "In my opinion," he replied, "we shall do it by thorough preparation, eternal vigilance and," he paused to emphasise the point, "waiting for the right moment to arrive."

'Aldworth', October 1891

The Tyndalls had been invited over to *Aldworth* for luncheon, and after the meal the two men moved to Tennyson's study while the ladies retired to the drawing room. John Tyndall and Alfred Tennyson had been friends for many years, and enjoyed each other's company. Today, however, both felt a little dejected as their advancing years and failing health became ever more obvious to them.

"An excellent luncheon Lord Tennyson, thank you," said Tyndall with feigned formality.

"Will you share a pipe with me while the ladies gossip?" his host asked.

Tyndall looked at the row of clay pipes in a rack on the mantelpiece. "You have enough of them," he remarked.

"I have fourteen," replied Tennyson. "I use a different one each day for a fortnight, then start the round again." With that, he took one of the pipes

down and began to fill it.

"I think my constitution will bear a pull or two."

"We're neither of us getting any younger, Tyndall."

"You're eleven years my senior, yet I think you carry your years better than I do. Dratted *gouty phlebitis* in my left leg - I have to take three opium pills and 16 grains of chloral during a day sometimes, just to give me some rest."

"Still active though," Tennyson replied giving his friend a sly look. "I hear continual reports of your speechmaking against Home Rule. *Punch* had something to say on the matter recently I recall."

One of Tyndall's screens at Hindhead

"And I said that, contrary to *Punch's* statement, I would unquestionably give Gladstone all the assistance I could render him, but only if we were tied together on the slopes of the Matterhorn!"

Tennyson's rich voice joined in the laughter. "The Matterhorn," he mused. "When we first met - what, over thirty years ago now? - you had not made your famous ascents in the Alps."

"I remember we talked about what makes the sky blue, and the size of the moon as it reaches the horizon," said Tyndall, "and you first introduced me to a pipe of your tobacco." At this, he took the proffered pipe which his host had lit for him. "Thank you."

"And you were not afraid to quote my *Maud* to me," replied the Poet Laureate.

"You said at the time you thought it was one of the best things you'd ever done."

"I feel that still."

"But then I looked at your two boys, and I called *them* the best poems you'll ever produce."

"How can a father deny that?" said the Laureate. His eyes were moist as he remembered Lionel, who had died of jungle fever on a voyage home from India five years before. Then looking at Tyndall he reflected, "You have no children."

"But I have the finest wife a man could wish for - a true companion in all things."

They pulled on their pipes in silence for a while, each reflecting on his own thoughts. "And how goes the saga of the Hindhead screens?" Tennyson said at last.

Tyndall grunted. "Continues to give newspaper editors several inches of copy a day, it seems. Hirst has persuaded me not to leap to my pen in reply."

"Very wise," agreed the lord.

But Tyndall became agitated. "I can't imagine how else I was supposed to protect my privacy. Trees would not grow quickly enough - it needed a 40 ft height to block the view."

"Which your larch poles and heather cladding instantly provided."

"They are things of beauty - I would say noble is not an unreasonable description. Even amid the wildest storm I feel no misgiving about them." He would defend his screens to the last.

"I cannot argue," said Tennyson. "I fled here from the Cockney Invasion on the Isle of Wight."

Silence returned as they pulled on their pipes again. This time it was Tyndall who spoke first. He noticed a painted portrait of his host in the room which he had not seen before. "Is that a new likeness of you I see over there?"

Alfred, Lord Tennyson by Helen Allingham, 1890

"By Helen Allingham. She finally persuaded me to sit still for her last year on one of her visits here."

"I remember a visit they both made to me just a few months before poor Allingham became so ill," Tyndall reflected. "They had walked from Sandhills up to the Hindhead Cross, and then came to meet me at my gate. I recall particularly - just as they arrived we were amazed to see two brown bears come shambling over the heath, and five foreign-looking men walking beside them."

"He took *me* up to Hindhead once," replied Tennyson, "before you were there - to look for some Gypsies he'd heard were around." He laughed. "We didn't find them."

"Broomsquires a'plenty there," said Tyndall. "Allingham wouldn't be mistaken, would he?"

"It's possible I suppose," the other replied, and took another pull on his pipe. "You know," he said at last, "I often repeat William's dying words, as Mrs Allingham recalls them. *'I see such things as you cannot dream of.'*"

Tyndall looked back at the painting. "It's a fine likeness."

"I sat for Watts a short time afterwards." Then reflectively he added, "I suppose they're all trying to get in before I die."

"There's a morbid thought."

"They may be right. I've done nothing much for the past two years - that was when I wrote *Crossing the Bar*, on the ferry over from Lymington. An allegory on crossing from life to death - d'you think it significant?"

But Tyndall had no time to answer, as the ladies interrupted them at this point. "Lady Tennyson and I were wondering if you two gentlemen had fallen asleep in here," said Louisa Tyndall as they came through the door.

"No, my dear Louisa," her husband assured her, "merely recalling times past and old glories."

"You were going to read to us today, were you not, Alfred?" Lady Tennyson remarked.

"I was indeed, Emily. Assuming these good people are prepared to suffer it with good grace."

"It will be a great pleasure, Lord Tennyson," Louisa replied.

"Something from the earlier days," suggested Tyndall.

"Not from my Juvenilia, I implore you."

Lady Tennyson was quite certain what was required. "How about the Duke of Wellington?" she suggested.

"The mighty funeral?" said her husband. He nodded assent, and started to search through a book for it, but Tyndall appeared to beat him to it.

"*Bury the Great Duke with an Empire's lamentation...*" he began.

Tennyson looked up, then chuckled. "I do not need the book - Mr Tyndall will recite for it us *vive voce*!"

"No, no, that's as far as I can go without a text, I assure you."

"And a rendition by John has hardly the *gravitas* of a rendition by the author," remarked Louisa.

The author had by this time found the passage, and with a slight bow to Louisa, he began to read from it in his wonderful bass voice,

> "*Bury the Great Duke with an Empire's lamentation,*
> *Let us bury the Great Duke to the noise of the*
> *mourning of a mighty nation,*
> *Mourning when their leaders fall,*
> *Warriors carry the warrior's pall,*
> *And sorrow darkens hamlet and hall...*"

Dr Roger Hutchinson's House
late on Wednesday 5th October 1892

As a local G.P., Dr Roger Hutchinson was used to being called out at all hours of day and night, so it was no particular surprise to him or his wife Eleanor to hear a loud knocking on their door late in the evening. Eleanor sighed and put aside her work. "I'm coming!" The knocking continued. "I'm coming, I'm coming!" It was a moonlit night, and when she opened the door she recognised the man outside as one of Lord Tennyson's servants.

"Doctor Hutchinson - is he at home?" The man was breathless.

She began to answer, but the man's message was too urgent, "He must come now, quickly - to Lord Tennyson."

"Lord Tennyson?" she replied. He had his own London physicians, and if it was anything serious they would surely have been called. "Has there been an accident?"

"Lady Tennyson sent me. She says he's dying. Could the doctor come."

Roger and Eleanor Hutchinson

"I'll get him." Eleanor reacted instinctively, and called indoors for her husband.

"She's sent for his doctor from London," explained the man, "but he won't get here for some hours. Lord Tennyson's been unwell for a few days, but now..."

Roger Hutchinson, appeared in the hall and saw the anxious faces. "Is there a problem?" he asked.

"Lord Tennyson, doctor," the man repeated.

"His wife believes him to be dying," said Eleanor, and knowing her husband would be concerned about the medical ethics of treating another doctor's patient, added, "his London surgeon has been called. I'll fetch your coat and mine - we shall go and see what we can do."

"Both of you?" asked the man.

"I am a trained nurse," said Eleanor, "and Lady Tennyson may also need some comfort." With this she went indoors to get ready.

Seeing the man had come on horseback, Roger told him they would follow him to *Aldworth* in their trap. "Tell Lady Tennyson we are on our way post-haste," he said.

They wound their way up through the lanes to the house on the hillside, and arrived to find Lady Tennyson sitting beside her husband's bed. The Poet Laureate lay there, bathed in moonlight from the oriel window, his expression serene, his breathing shallow, clasping a copy of the Shakespeare which he had asked for earlier in the day. Roger made a brief examination, but knowing that Sir Andrew Clark had been telegraphed, he was reluctant to do more.

"Eleanor will stay with you while I go to meet the surgeon off the London train," he said to Lady Tennyson. Her eyes turned briefly from the marble-like figure - "Thank you, doctor, I am most grateful" - then returned to their vigil. Sensing Eleanor beside her, she said, "The world will remember him as a great poet, but I knew him as a kind husband and a good father."

"Then you have had a joy denied to the rest of the world," said Eleanor softly.

A Room in London, November 1893

Octavia Hill was more content with progress now. Indeed today's meeting at the offices of the Commons Preservation Society promised to be the final hurdle before Hunter's idea of a National Trust could at last be implemented. With her in the ante-room was her staunch ally Hardwicke Rawnsley. Some properties had suddenly come up for sale in his Lake District, and he had contacted Hunter asking for urgent action - this meeting was the result.

She also knew that Rawnsley had recently received a promotion. "So you are now an honorary canon of Carlisle Cathedral. My congratulations."

"Thank you, Miss Hill."

"I confess, however, that I am not entirely clear what the duties of an Honorary Canon are."

Rawnsley smiled. "There are no duties in the Cathedral as such," he said. "It is a purely titular rank - I am part of the chapter there, but unlike a full canon I do not have to reside there. And," he added, "I receive no emoluments for it either."

"Ah, there's the rub!" she replied.

"But it leaves me free to pursue other important matters," he continued, "such as these properties in the Lake District, for example."

Octavia nodded her approval. "As you know, we sent out notices to all the likely supporters we could think of."

"It is well attended too," he said with satisfaction.

Octavia looked around at the faces. "I'm glad to see Mr Shaw Lefevre is here," she said. "I had been concerned for his interest."

"Surely, he cannot be other than deeply interested," replied Rawnsley. "As chairman of the Commons Preservation Society, the whole idea of a 'National Trust' must find great favour with him."

"I think he felt it might compete for resources with his existing Society."

"Then we must disillusion him," the canon replied, and seeing Hunter entering the room, added, "and here's the very man to do it. Good day to you, Mr Hunter."

"Good day to you - *Canon* Rawnsley now, is it not?"

"It is," then in a lower tone, "I gather there is talk in the corridors of a possible honour coming *your* way in the New Year - if it is not out of order for me to mention it."

Hunter never failed to be amazed how the best-kept secrets leaked out. "Quite out of order I'm afraid, canon," he told him with a twinkle in his eye. "Such things are never discussed."

"What we *were* just discussing," said Octavia pointedly, "was my concern for Mr Shaw Lefevre's commitment to our cause."

Hunter turned to her. "I don't think you need worry too much about that, Miss Hill. He seems to have been brought round to our point of view now."

"And not before time," she remarked scathingly, "it's taken ten years! How many properties have been lost to us in that time?"

"We have to regard that as water under the bridge, I fear," replied Hunter. "Today we debate in earnest the formation of a new body which will, I quote, '*act as a corporation for the holding of lands of natural beauty and sites and houses of historic interest to be preserved intact for the Nation's use and enjoyment.*'" It had been Hunter himself who had drawn up the form of words.

"You have some American example to show us, I believe?" said Octavia.

"A Massachusetts act passed two years ago, called the Trustees of Public Reservations Act."

Rawnsley had been looking around. "Mr Ruskin will be happy to see some of his own ideas enshrined in our plan. Is he not here with us today?" At this, Octavia examined the floor. She had at one time enjoyed a close relationship with John Ruskin - but since his refusal to help her save Swiss Cottage Fields, and even worse his embarrassing publication of their letters after a major disagreement a few years later, she had no wish to meet him here.

"Ruskin?" echoed Hunter, "I believe not, but we are not short of other notable people." He pointed to the other side of the room. "Huxley is here, and so is Watts - and this is just a preliminary affair. I understand the Duke of Westminster has offered his house in Park Lane for any full inaugural meeting we may arrange later."

"That would be a welcome boost to our public image," said Rawnsley.

"In fact," continued Hunter, "he has already agreed to be the first name put forward to serve on the provisional council of the Trust."

Octavia pulled herself together at this. "At last I begin to feel we are getting somewhere," she declared.

"The road ahead is still a long one," warned Hunter, "but I believe we now have the right vehicle with which to travel it."

"Not a railway engine I hope!" quipped Rawnsley.

Hunter smiled. "The railway has its place, Rawnsley, but not, I agree, by the sides of your lakes." Then sensing a general movement out of the room he added, "I believe the meeting is ready to start now. Shall we go in?"

Hind Head House, 4th December 1893

John Tyndall had been in poor health for a number of years. His doctor had prescribed magnesia for his digestion and chloral to help him sleep, and the dedicated Louisa administered these to him daily. Today, a fresh bottle of chloral had been procured, and so instead of the usual two bottles on the table there were three, and by mistake, she had poured him a dose from the chloral bottle thinking it was magnesia.

Dr Winstanley had been called to the house immediately, and Jonathan Hutchinson came over later in the morning. He found Louisa in the sitting room, despair on her face.

"How could I do it, Dr Hutchinson?" she sobbed.

He took her arm and tried to console her. "An easy mistake, my dear Mrs Tyndall. You must not rebuke yourself too much for making it. Medicine bottles all look very similar."

"He knew as soon as I'd done it," she managed to tell him between tears. "He just looked at me and said, 'My poor darling, you have killed your John.'"

"Chloral you say?"

"I gave him a full dose thinking it was magnesia."

"This morning?"

"At eight thirty."

Hutchinson sighed. "We shall do all we can. Dr Winstanley is already in with him you say?"

"He is. I sent the trap for him immediately - he brought all the devices he could think of."

"Tell me again what you have done so far."

"I tried tickling his throat, but it did nothing. I looked for an emetic in *Whitaker's* and gave him a dose of mustard as it recommended, but that did nothing either." She stopped to wipe her eyes, then continued, "The maids and I put him in bed and got hot-water bottles all round him."

"He took nothing else?" insisted Hutchinson.

"He was able to take some hot coffee. But soon after that he lost consciousness."

Hutchinson scratched his head. "Who is his regular physician?"

"Dr Buzzard - I have sent a message to him in London."

"He will not be here before five o'clock at the earliest," replied Hutchinson, checking his watch. Then turning to the distraught wife he said gently, "You realise of course that your husband was not a well man, even before this event."

She burst into tears again. "Poor John," she sobbed, "we kept saying we would write our biography - but we never did."

Hutchinson waited while she tried to regain control. "A tolerably strong man might survive an overdose such as this," he said, "but Mr Tyndall's constitution has been so very weakened of late..."

"He will not live, will he," she cut in, looking him in the eye.

Hutchinson spread his hands. "While there's life there's hope, Mrs Tyndall - but I think you should prepare yourself to expect the worst." She nodded weakly. "Come," he said rising, "let us see how Dr Winstanley is faring."

> They worked all day trying everything they knew, but by 6.30 pm it was all over. John Tyndall was dead, and it was left to Louisa to try to write their biography alone.
>
> His 'noble' screens of birch and heather, complete with lightning conductors, survived him by seven years, finally succumbing to a gale during the first month of 1901 - in the same week that Queen Victoria passed away.

Haslemere High Street, July 1894

James Stewart Hodgson had, by 1889, become the lord of two manors and the largest landowner in the vicinity of Haslemere. He was also renowned locally as a man with a keen sense of humour who was generous, genial and good.

However, he was a partner in the house of Baring, which had recently collapsed, and though he had always swayed on the side of caution, he had been 'overcome by the stronger will of Lord Revelstoke' and had finally to share the responsibility with him.

With 'fine philosophy', he auctioned off his collections and nearly all his estate, and retired to a smaller house in Haslemere. Walking down the High Street one day soon afterwards, he met Penfold and the rector, Mr Etheridge, coming up the street together.

"My dear Hodgson," the rector greeted him, "I find you surprisingly chirpy for a man who has just sold all his possessions."

Hodgson shook hands with them both. "I still have more than enough to keep body and soul together, rector - and a fine wife to look after me in my old age."

"You're living at the old Manor House now, I understand," said Penfold.

"Beautiful place, don't you think?" replied Hodgson.

Penfold gave his view as an architect. "One of the finest little sixteenth century houses around in my opinion."

Hodgson smiled. "I think so too - glad you agree."

"But from being the lord of the manors of Godalming and Haslemere," said Etheridge, "with Lord knows how many other pieces of land to your name - three thousand acres wasn't it? - to suddenly go from all that to a single sixteenth century cottage..."

"... is the whirligig of life," said Hodgson, completing the rector's sentence for him. "I intend to be quite philosophical about it - I am now in retirement. When the company failed..."

"I think I should have been cast into deepest depression in your position," Etheridge cut in, "I freely admit it."

"But with my friends about me in this village," Hodgson continued, "I had no fear of being left in want."

"As the recent meeting in the *White Horse* showed," added Penfold.

"Yes, I was most touched by that. To be invited along and shown so much kindness by everyone..."

"You must worry, though," the rector insisted, "that your good works - all those thousands of trees you planted for example - will be ruined by the new owners of your land."

Penfold replied for him. "In practice there's probably precious little we or anyone else can do - if Mr Hutchinson and his family want to start building on the land of yours he bought at Half Moon Estate, for instance."

"There's no harm in a certain amount of develop-

Rev Sanders Etheridge,
first rector of Haslemere

John Wornham Penfold
in 1873

ment going on in Haslemere," Hodgson ventured. "After all, it needed something to raise the village from its lethargy when I moved here thirty years ago, and the process won't stop just because the turn of the century is soon upon us."

"These kaleidoscopic days of shifting population," said the rector, "it can be difficult to live with sometimes."

"But live we must," remarked Hodgson. "This new idea of local democracy for example - it's going to change things even more, is it not?"

"I'm not sure I feel entirely comfortable with the concept," admitted Etheridge. "It appears there are to be two parishes of Haslemere - one for the church and one for the state."

"It will, I'm sure, be an amicable arrangement," said Hodgson.

Penfold also felt positive about it. "It gives the electors of Haslemere the power to govern the secular side of their life," he said to Etheridge, "but you still guard their souls."

"What's important," added Hodgson, "is that we set the new parish council up properly - with a good man at its head."

Etheridge hesitated. "I had wondered about proposing Sir Robert," he said.

"An excellent choice," exclaimed Penfold. "There would be few who could disagree with that."

"He's a man of great energy," continued the rector, "but I gather he is also greatly involved in London with the idea of this new National Trust."

The National Trust is founded

Following the preliminary meeting of 16th November 1893, Hugh Lupus Grosvenor, first Duke of Westminster offered the use of his Grosvenor House for an inaugural meeting which finally constituted the Trust. This was held on 16th July 1894, with the Duke in the chair.

On 12th January 1895, the trust was registered under the Companies Acts by the Board of Trade. A legislative sub-committee was then set up to discuss special legislation needed for a charitable trust holding land, and the first meeting of the Executive Committee was held the following month under the chairmanship of Sir Robert Hunter.

"And he has a very demanding job of work as solicitor to the Post Office," added Hodgson.

"It was for *that* that he was knighted of course," Penfold said.

"Indeed," agreed Etheridge, "and I ask myself, will he have the time to devote to yet another duty? I wonder his poor wife ever gets to see him as it is."

Penfold gave a laugh. "We usually find it expedient to contact him at the Reform Club in London - I imagine he must virtually live there at times."

"I ought to consider whether I think it fair even to ask him," mused the rector.

Hodgson had a clear opinion on the matter. "If you want a job done, Mr Etheridge, they say give it to a busy man."

"Very true," the rector admitted.

"And having said that," Hodgson added preparing to leave them, "I may be in retirement now, but I still find there are not enough hours in my day - so if you gentlemen will excuse me..."

"And I must carry on with my research into Haslemere history," declared Penfold. "The rector is about to introduce me to yet another volume of church registers to be copied down."

Hodgson laughed. "Rather you than me, Mr Penfold - I prefer to associate with the living than the dead." He lifted his hat. "Good day to you both."

Workmen's Club, Haslemere,
8th December, 1894

At the end of 1894, Haslemere, along with many other villages and boroughs throughout the country, was coming to terms with the idea of creating new parish and district councils, and a public meeting was held to address the question.

Alfred Softly took the chair, and with him on the dais was the rector.

"Ladies and gentlemen," said Mr Softly, waiting for the hall to quieten down, "thank you. Now by virtue of my office as Senior Overseer of the parish of Haslemere, I have been asked to take the chair temporarily at the start of this historic meeting - and I'm glad to see so many of you here tonight taking an interest - hardly a spare seat in the hall." He looked at the sea of faces in front of him. "But of course," he continued with a smile, "my first duty is immediately to ask you to let me off, and elect your own chairman for the evening."

Haslemere High Street, circa 1894

The meeting laughed with him, and when silence was restored, the rector stood up. "Mr Chairman," he said loudly, "I should like to propose Sir Robert Hunter. He is most learned in the law, especially familiar with the affairs of the parish, and universally respected by all the parishioners. I can think of no-one better to preside over these deliberations."

There were cries of "Hear, hear." "Thank you Mr Etheridge," replied the chairman. "Do I have a seconder?" The Hon. Rollo Russell raised his hand from the body of the hall, and was thanked in turn.

"Any objections from the floor?" There were none. "Carried unanimously then, thank you." He sought out Hunter's eye in the audience. "Sir Robert, may I offer you both my congratulations, and my chair?"

There was spontaneous applause as Hunter rose and walked to the rostrum. He shook the hand of Mr Softly, who moved aside.

Hunter waited for the hubbub to die down again. "Ladies and gentlemen," he began, "I accept with thanks the expression of confidence in my judgement and impartiality which you have so cordially given me, and in assuming the chair I have great pleasure in placing my services, and my experience in the interpretation of the law, at the disposal of you, my fellow-parishioners, in this the first act of a drama which is about to revolutionise the parish life of rural England."

"Now my duties this evening are by no means a sinecure," he continued, "and so I ask you to allow the rector and the senior overseer, Mr Softly, to act as my assessors for the evening." He paused here to allow for any comments, but none came, and he continued, "The first, and by far most important issue to be determined of course, is whether or not you wish there to be a poll of the parish for the new council. I shall call for a show of hands in a moment..."

At this, Rayner Storr rose. "Yes, Mr Storr?"

The latter spoke genially, but with determination. "Mr Chairman, we have here a written demand for a poll, signed by 26 electors and ready to be handed in - that would seem adequate - is it really necessary to proceed with a show of hands?"

"I'm afraid the instructions are quite clear," replied Hunter, "and it is a formality which cannot legally be dispensed with."

"Well may I say, Mr Chairman," said Storr, "that I shall decline to hold up my hand for so futile and misleading an object." There was a murmur of agreement in the hall, and Hunter held up his hand before continuing. "I quite understand your point, Mr Storr, and I take no offence by it."

"No offence to the chair intended," Storr replied.

"Perhaps we can, nonetheless, press on *positively*," Hunter continued, causing a ripple of laughter, since Storr was known to be a Positivist by persuasion, "*positively* with the requirements laid before us, in order to complete the formalities as swiftly as possible." He looked around for any further questions, and there were none. The meeting continued harmoniously to a conclusion less than two hours later.

First Haslemere Parish Council

In the subsequent poll, the following were elected:
  Stewart Hodgson, gentleman;
  Turner Bridger, auctioneer and estate agent;
  Allen Chandler, barrister;
  James Stuart Edgeler, saddler;
  Peter Aylwin, chemist;
  John Moorey, bricklayer;
  John Wornham Penfold, architect and surveyor;
  R W Winstanley, surgeon;
  W S A Ardagh, surgeon and physician.

Sir Robert Hunter was elected by the Council to be its first Chairman.

Two years later the 'Surrey Times' said: "No Parish Council in the county has done better work than Haslemere, due ... to the invaluable work of Sir Robert Hunter as Chairman."

Haslemere Museum, November 1895

Having outgrown the barn at *Inval*, Jonathan Hutchinson's educational museum had recently moved to new purpose-built premises on a hill overlooking Haslemere High Street - land which had previously been part of Stewart Hodgson's estate.

As a birthday treat, Hutchinson's grandson Allen Chandler, now eight years old, was being taken on a guided tour by his grandfather.

"How d'you like my new museum then, young Allen?" the old man asked him after they had seen most of the exhibits.

The boy thought for a while. "It looks the same inside as the old one to me," he said innocently.

Hutchinson 'tut-tutted.' "Now, now - don't disappoint your old grandfather. There's far more space here in the new buildings - now we can show things off properly."

"But it's got the same stripes painted on the walls, and all the same things I've seen before on the shelves..."

"And many more things you've *not* seen before, because I've not had the room to display them," said his grandfather with mock sternness.

Little Allen shrugged his shoulders. "I prefer listening to you talk about it all - it's dull just looking."

"There I agree with you," said Hutchinson with approval. "To have a Museum without a lecturer is like having a church without a minister." Perhaps a strange analogy for this man with his Quaker background to use.

"Can I come here next Sunday and hear you talk?" the lad asked eagerly.

Keeping a straight face, Hutchinson replied, "My boy, you can come next Sunday and *give* the lecture!"

The boy's face fell a mile. "*Give* it?" he asked incredulously.

"Yes, why not?"

"*Me* give it? I couldn't possibly."

"Certainly you could."

This was serious, thought Allen. "What could I talk about?" he said.

Jonathan Hutchinson in later life

"Oh anything," replied his grandfather diffidently, "say - Palaeogenesis."

"Palio-what?"

"How the zebra got its stripes."

"But - I don't know anything about zebras."

"That, my boy," said Hutchinson with emphasis, "is the very reason why you should talk about them."

"But..."

Hutchinson chuckled and ruffled the boy's hair. "Don't worry, lad, I'm teasing you. Next Sunday *I* shall talk, and the subjects will be: The Thickness of the Earth's Crust; John Wesley; and Elephants."

"There's the elephant's skull, over there," said Allen, pointing.

"D'you remember helping me to unpack it, last year at *Inval*?"

"It was all dusty, and we had to clean it. Why hasn't it got any tusks?"

Hutchinson went over to the examine it. "Ivory is too valuable these days - we poor scientific people couldn't afford a skull with tusks. This old chap probably didn't grow any, as you can see."

The boy thought about it for a while, then said, "What are tusks?"

His grandfather was never one to give an immediate answer if he thought the questioner could work it out himself. "What would you say?" he asked.

"Er - big teeth?"

"You're right. The tusks are the elephant's two upper central incisor teeth." He took a sheet of notepaper out of his pocket. "Do you want to try answering some more questions? I've a whole list of them here - they're written for the Christmas examination this year."

Questions asked in Nov/Dec 1899

1. Do Whales have teeth?
2. Is the ice of an iceberg salty?
3. From what gulf does the Gulf Stream flow?
4. In what country are the Niagara Falls?
5. To what family of animals does the Otter belong?
6. How many feet are there in a mile?
7. How many inches are there in a fathom?
8. Did King John have any children?

"Are they easy?"

"That depends how much notice you've been taking during your visit to the museum." The boy looked dubious. "They are meant to be answered by young people," his grandfather added.

"I might need some help."

Hutchinson looked around. "Well," he said, "I notice there are others here in the museum today - perhaps *they* can help you with some of the more difficult questions."

The boy agreed reluctantly, and a number of other visitors were drawn into a group and given an impromptu examination. Eight questions were read out one by one. Allen was given the first chance to answer, then the others could make their guesses.

At the end, his grandfather was forced to admit, "I really do not think you *quite* qualify as a prize-winner this year, young Allen. Perhaps next year." Then, seeing the boy was weary, he said, "Come now, it's time for me to take you back to your mother."

As the two left the building to walk down the hill to the town, young Allen looked up at his grandfather and smiled. "Not everyone's granddad owns a museum," he thought to himself. Then clearing all other things from his mind he concentrated instead on wondering what would be on the table for his birthday tea.

Lea Park, Witley, May 1899

Under the headline *'Despoiling Hindhead Common,'* a local newspaper of 13th May 1899, reported that:—

'Many residents of Hindhead are not a little annoyed, and certainly very much grieved, at the poor respect which the new lord of the manor is apparently showing for the natural beauty and adornments of Hindhead Common and the Punch Bowl.'

This lord of the manor was Whitaker Wright, and Sir Frederick Pollock decided to go and talk with him at Lea Park to find out why he appeared to be being so disagreeable. He met a portly figure, immaculately dressed in a frock coat, wearing pince-nez spectacles and, despite having spent twenty three years in America, still speaking with a discernible English North Country accent.

"Now, Sir Frederick, what is the substance of this complaint?" asked Wright when they had introduced themselves.

"Well, Mr Wright," replied Pollock, "many residents of Hindhead have protested at seeing gangs of men using your 'infernal machine,' as they call it, to dig up whole rows of holly trees along the ridge of Gibbet Hill and down in the Bowl."

Lea Park, circa 1892

Wright looked puzzled. "I can assure you that I have no personal knowledge of this happening - none at all."

"It is not taking place at your request then?"

"I have made provision for a certain amount of soil to be transferred here to Lea Park, for the purposes of making some improvements, but nothing more."

"But these trees are such a characteristic feature of the spot, and they are being lifted bodily from their place along with the soil."

"That was never my intention. I'll put a stop to it."

"Two tons of soil at a time are being carted away," continued Pollock.

"I said I'll put a stop to it, and I shall," said Wright, his voice starting to become agitated.

Pollock had not finished. "And the heather surface on the Gibbet itself has also been removed in places, where quarrying for stone is going on."

Wright seemed stung by this. "I believe as lord of the manor I'm entitled to certain rights on my own property," he said bluntly.

"There are also commoners' rights over that part of your property, Mr Wright," explained Pollock patiently. "They should have been explained to you at the time you purchased it recently."

"Look, Sir Frederick," Wright said, beginning to colour, "I've no wish to make myself unpopular with the people round here, you should know that." Pollock knew nothing of the sort, but Wright continued, "Goodness knows, here in Witley you'd be hard put to find a man with a word against me."

"Unfortunately," countered Pollock, "the same cannot be said of Hindhead, Mr Wright."

Wright felt he should try another tack. "I'm away from my estate much of the time - you know how it is - and my instructions have been misinterpreted."

"Well I have no wish to appear unduly harsh," conceded Pollock, "if a genuine mistake has been made..."

"I can assure you that is the situation..."

"But a good deal of damage has already been done, and probably cannot now be undone."

Wright stared at him through his pince-nez. "If regrets could alter the past, Sir Frederick, we should all live happier men."

Pollock sensed there might perhaps be more behind this statement than met the eye, but replied simply, "I'll not argue with that, Mr Wright."

"Then let's shake hands and put this sorry episode behind us." Wright was bluff and genial again. "Now, you haven't seen my room under the lake yet, have you?"

"I had heard of it."

"Hearing about it is nothing, you must see it. Have you time before you go?" Pollock confirmed that he had. "Good," said Wright, "I shall show you," and he led the way into the grounds, explaining as they went every detail of the intricate underground construction.

A playing field near The Royal Huts,
Hindhead, September 1900

Young Allen Chandler, now known to his friends as Rex, went to school in Hindhead and played football there on a field by the *Royal Huts Hotel*. On the other side of the road, in a new house called *Undershaw*, lived a tall professor with a drooping moustache and a mischievous chuckle.

He used to join in their games from time to time with great energy, and the boys were not at all sure that they appreciated his interest.

"Watch it, it's the Prof again!" Rex called to his friends one day.

"Don't let him get the ball!" yelled another.

The chuckle preceded the man. "Playing football again, are we?"

"We'd just finished, sir," said Rex, holding the ball tightly in his arms.

"I could do with a bit of exercise though," said the man, and he took the ball and placed it back on the ground. "Right, who's in goal?" The boys moved reluctantly to their places on the pitch, and the professor began to impress them with his nimble footwork.

"Oh no, mind your keys!" shouted Rex as he was challenged.

"What's wrong with my keys?"

"That big bunch in your trouser pocket, it's all knobbly," Rex replied, "it hurts when you tackle us."

"Digs into our shoulders, what with you being so tall," said his friend.

Sir Arthur Conan Doyle

"Well, you'll have to take more care then, won't you!"

The boys looked at each other, but before play could continue, a slim figure appeared on the touch-line, holding a piece of paper which she waved in the air. "Mr Conan Doyle?" she asked nervously.

The professor recognised her as the girl from the village post office, and walked over. The boys ran off with the ball as fast as they could, not yet realising that they had just been playing football with the famous inventor of Sherlock Holmes.

Flora Timms knew well enough who he was, and almost felt like curtseying in his presence. "Your wife said I should find you here, sir." She handed him the telegram. "Shall I wait for a reply?"

Memorial to Flora Thompson in Liphook, Hampshire

Conan Doyle opened it up and read the message. "Ha! From Bernard Shaw, giving me his new address." He looked at the girl. "No, no reply at the moment, thank you. When is it you close?"

"Six o'clock, sir."

"Then I shall walk down to you later with my answer," he said with a glint in his eye, "and watch you toy with your tinkling telegraph needle."

"That's incoming messages, sir," she told him solemnly.

"I was teasing you, Miss Timms. You are too serious. What do you do to lighten your day when you are not being our Grayshott postmistress?"

Flora didn't know what to say. She could hardly tell this great author that she, also, liked to write. "I walk," she said simply.

"A healthy, but lonely pursuit. No other?"

"Well..." She hesitated again. Could she tell him? No, she couldn't! "I also read," she said finally.

"You read!" he exclaimed, "that's capital. More should do it. I shall see you later at your post," he quipped, "when I have penned a suitable reply to Shaw." With that he pocketed the telegram and made across the field for home.

She turned, deep in thought, to walk back to Grayshott down Headley Road. Headley was the mother village, and she had heard that the name meant 'a clearing in the heather.' Looking now at the heath in bloom around her, she could quite understand why.

> *Later, when she had become well-known as an author in her own right, Flora Thompson recalled her time in Grayshott in a book which she called 'Heatherley'.*

Haslemere Station, 16th March 1902

Hunter and Pollock both travelled up to work in London, and this morning as they met on the platform at Haslemere station there was only one topic of conversation.

"Heard the news Robert? They've picked him up in New York, along with his niece."

"What's the charge?" asked Hunter.

"It just says here a charge of 'being a fugitive from justice.'"

Hunter shook his head. "Seems very fishy to me."

Pollock carried on reading from his newspaper, "When the French steamer *La Lorraine* arrived at New York, detectives went on board and arrested Mr Wright who was travelling under an assumed name."

"He's an American citizen," Hunter said, "though you'd never guess it from the way he speaks."

"They'll have a problem extraditing him then."

"I imagine that's what he hopes - why he bolted for America when the chips were down."

Pollock folded his paper. "What's your opinion?"

Hunter looked at him. "Of Whitaker Wright?"

"No, of his position."

"I think it'll be a difficult case," said Hunter carefully. "Devilishly complicated thing, fraud - the result will probably depend on who are the counsels and the Judge involved."

Haslemere Station in early 20th C

"In other words, a bit of a lottery. Hardly an advertisement for blind British justice."

Hunter gave a laugh. "We are both in the legal profession, Frederick - what do you think?"

Pollock pondered for a while. "I agree with you," he said - then after a little more thought, "And what becomes of his estate?"

"If he's found guilty, you mean?"

"He's not been an ideal lord of the manor, but..."

Hunter nodded. "The devil you know."

"Exactly. We've at least come to terms with Mr Wright - we could get a lot worse if Hindhead Common were to change hands."

"They've got to get him to court first," observed Hunter. The handbell was being rung and a plume of black smoke could be seen rising from behind the trees to the south west, coming nearer. "Here's the train - front end as usual?"

"I think so," replied Pollock, and they walked in step down the platform to stand out of habit at the very spot where the first class compartment would stop.

Near The Royal Huts, Hindhead, 1902

The sound of a klaxon on the road was still a rare enough event at Hindhead for people to turn round and take notice. Rex Chandler and his friends stopped playing their game of cricket to watch as a large green-bodied car with red wheels chugged slowly along.

Seven-seater automobile of the period

"Here, it's the professor back again," said Rex. "What's he got there?"

"It's a Rolls," said one of his friends, knowingly.

"Nah," said another, "it's a Wolseley."

"How d'you know that?"

"See by the insignia!"

"Smart isn't it?"

"Big one too - seven seater."

"Look, it's stopping - he's getting out."

And sure enough the chugging had ceased, and the driver, in goggles and peaked cap, had risen from his seat.

"Hang on, he might come over here," said Rex suddenly, "hide that cricket ball!"

"Does he play cricket too?"

"Yes, he plays for the village."

Rex knew better. "He's played for the MCC!"

"How d'you know that?"

"My uncle Roger told me."

Conan Doyle had been trying in vain to restart his car, and now he was indeed walking across towards the boys.

"Smashing car you've got there," said Rex to him when he was within ear-shot.

"It *is* a Wolseley isn't it," asked his friend.

"It is," confirmed Conan Doyle. "Ten horse power."

"Where've you driven from?"

"From Birmingham."

The boys gasped. "Birmingham!?" It might have been the other side of the world. "All the way?"

The driver smiled. "All the way."

"How long's it taken you?"

"A very long time - and now I'm nearly home, it's stopped. Would you lads like to give me a push? It's only a few more yards."

"Rather!" they cried.

"Just get me across the road and into my drive, then it's downhill."

They followed him back to his car. "He must have a bit of money to buy one of these," said one lad to another.

'Undershaw,' Conan Doyle's house at Hindhead

"Well, he's the most famous author in the country, isn't he. He must have lots of money," the other replied.

"I reckon everybody will have something like this one day," said Rex.

"What, *everyone* Rex?" his friend mocked him, "don't be stupid - that's not possible."

"Why not?" he asked. By this time they had reached the vehicle, and were gathered round the back to wait for instructions.

"I'll tell you why not," said the other, "because if everybody had one, who'd be left to push them?" He ducked just in time to miss a cuff round the ear.

The command "Push!" came from in front, and slowly but surely they eased the ton weight along the dusty road and down into the drive of *Undershaw*.

A room in the Law Courts, Strand, London
26th January 1904

The trial had gone badly for Whitaker Wright, and when the jury found him guilty at the end, he bowed meekly and allowed himself to be led back to the private room which he had used during the course of the proceedings.

"Well," he said quietly to his defence lawyer as he came through the door, "you heard the verdict - I am to do penal servitude for seven years."

"It's not a ruling which flatters English justice," replied Lawson Walton, his counsel.

Pen sketch of Whitaker Wright in 1904

"I was as innocent as any person in the Court, yet twelve good men and true found me guilty."

John Eyre, one of his oldest friends who had stood bail for him during the trial, was there to put a comforting hand on his shoulder. "Should we not telephone your wife to tell her before they take you away, Whitaker," he urged.

Wright shrugged off the hand. "There'll be plenty of time for that, John." He looked at the court official, there to guard him. "Would you object if I use the lavatory for a moment? It has been a long day." There seemed no good reason to refuse, so the man accompanied him out of the room and stood outside the toilet door.

Eyre sighed. "The prosecution seemed to have had the judge on their side," he remarked to Walton.

"He certainly appeared hostile to us on the defence."

"He kept playing to the gallery, trying to make them laugh at poor Whitaker."

Walton nodded. "We got off to a bad start when the prosecution asked that very first question, 'Why did you run away, and under an assumed name?' Mr Wright really should have prepared a better answer than the one he gave. After that the case simply slipped away from us."

"The poor man looked more and more frustrated and bewildered as the trial went on."

"But at the summing up he suddenly appeared so very calm and resigned," said Walton.

"I noticed that too, and just now he seemed to be speaking more in sorrow than anger."

They were interrupted by Wright's return, a look of unnatural serenity on his face. He moved straight over to a side-table where his bottle of whisky stood. "I think I deserve a last drink before I go, don't you?" he said, pouring himself a large one. "And John," he added, "perhaps you'd be good enough to get me out one of those cigars of mine."

John Eyre busied himself with this, while Wright tossed the drink back in a single gulp. Putting the glass down, he took out his watch and chain and held it out. "Here John, I shan't have any use for this where I'm going."

Eyre looked up in horror. "Whitaker, no I can't..." But Wright pushed it at him and barked, "I insist!" He took the watch and handed Wright the cigar.

"And now if you would do me a final favour..." Wright indicated for a light, but as Eyre struck the match, he slumped into a chair.

"A doctor - get a doctor, quickly!" Eyre shouted. The court official, with only the briefest of pauses, ran out to find one, and Walton bent down over the slouched form. "I fear it will be too late, Mr Eyre," he said, "there is a smell of almonds on his breath."

"Cyanide!"

"And what's this?" Feeling beneath the dying man's jacket, Walton brought out a gun. "A revolver, cocked and loaded! He certainly wasn't taking any chances."

"How the devil did he get that in here?"

But Walton was already hiding it in his own jacket pocket. "I think we should put this somewhere safe," he said, "to avoid further complications."

"Is he..."

Walton nodded, rising to his feet. "Stopped breathing now. A quick end."

View from Gibbet Hill in 1937

"Poor Whitaker," Eyre was fighting back tears, "he didn't deserve this."

"It's not always the most guilty who are punished," said Walton sagely.

They looked at the man, lifeless in the chair. "He will be deeply mourned in Witley," said Eyre, "and his going will touch the lives of very many in the area."

The Educational Hall, Haslemere
Saturday 14th October 1905

John Eyre's words were prophetic in a way he did not realise at the time. Due to the state of Wright's business affairs, his estate was to be sold off by the Chancery Division, but failing to sell it as a whole, they put it up for auction in fifty separate lots. One of these included Hindhead Common, and the Commons Preservation Society, supported by Sir Robert Hunter, appealed to residents in and around the area to guarantee enough money to buy it.

They called a special public meeting in Haslemere, at which a small committee was formed to take 'appropriate action'. Afterwards, Hunter spoke to Francis Muir and Laurence Chubb, an Australian.

"Well gentlemen, a very successful meeting I hope you'll agree."

"It's a relief to know that some things can be arranged quickly in a crisis," said Muir.

"Still a lot to do though, Francis, we've only a fortnight before the auction."

"How much d'you figure you'll need to be sure of getting it, Sir Robert?" said Chubb.

"My guess would be two to three thousand pounds, Lawrence. The more the better of course." Then, realising that his two friends did not know each other, he added, "By the way, I had no time to introduce you formally before the meeting, did I? Lawrence Chubb, secretary of the Commons Preservation Society and a past secretary of the National Trust - Francis Muir, vice-chairman of the Haslemere Commons and Footpaths Preservation Society."

"Pleased to meet you, Mr Chubb," said Muir - "Likewise, Mr Muir," replied Chubb as they shook hands.

"There are five of us on the sub-committee," continued Hunter, "and we'll have our work cut out

to find enough guarantors in the time."

"We have some very influential people living in and around Haslemere though," added Muir. "I'm sure the money can be obtained."

"We shall work through the list," Hunter said. "Mr Methuen has agreed that we may effect the purchase in his name, given sufficient support can be found."

Horse-drawn bus at Hindhead, 1905

"Will he attend the auction himself?" asked Muir.

"He cannot, and neither can I," Hunter admitted. "You will be our spokesman there, Francis - and Mr Chubb here will be with you." They both nodded. "As you know," added Hunter, "it is then our intention to convey the land to the National Trust as soon as possible afterwards."

"I only wish the Trust could help with this purchase in a more direct manner," said Chubb.

"You know the limitations of the situation as well as I do, Lawrence - they can accept a gift, but have no money of their own to put forward at the moment. Your personal help will be invaluable to us though, of that I am certain."

"I sincerely hope so."

With that, the three men went their separate ways, Chubb taking the train back to London and the others returning to their homes in Haslemere, knowing that in only twelve days time Whitaker Wright's estate would go under the hammer.

The Auction at Godalming
Thursday 26th October 1905

The Borough Hall at Godalming was packed, and among those present were many of the best-known residents of the neighbourhood, as well as influential businessmen from London. The auction had been in progress for a while now, and forty-six of the fifty lots had been dealt with. Mr Holland Peck, acting as auctioneer, addressed a sea of faces from his rostrum.

"And now, ladies and gentlemen, continuing with the auction of the late Mr Whitaker Wright's Lea Park Estate in Witley, by order of the Chancery Division, we come to Lot 47. Manorial rights over Hindhead Common, including the Devil's Punch Bowl, Gibbet Hill, Inval Common, and part of Weydown Common: 750 acres in all, timber included. Do I hear £2,000?"

Francis Muir and Lawrence Chubb looked at each other. They had managed to collect guarantees to the tune of just over £2,200. "Leaves us a bit tight," said Chubb.

"We might as well make a start though," said Muir.

"I have two thousand there," the auctioneer chanted. "Do I hear two hundred? Thank you sir - four hundred? Yes sir - six over there - two thousand six hundred. Any advance on two thousand six hundred?"

"I think we should stay in, don't you?" said Muir.

"Yes, I do," Chubb agreed, and put his hand up.

"Two thousand eight hundred to the gentleman there," said the auctioneer. "Do I hear three thousand? Three thousand? Yes I have three thousand at the back."

Muir sucked his teeth. "I fear we have been outbid, Mr Chubb. We cannot reasonably knock Mr Methuen for a thousand more than his guarantees."

Chubb looked around. "Just a minute, Mr Muir - I think I see an angel over there." He rose from his seat and moved across a few rows.

Muir's eyes followed him. "Perhaps Australian angels carry purses?" he thought to himself, but deep down suspected the lot was now lost to them.

The auctioneer was continuing the bidding. "I have three thousand. Can I hear five hundred? For this valuable and historic piece of land - do I hear three thousand five hundred?"

Muir saw that Chubb was returning to his seat with a lady. "May I introduce Mrs Thackeray Turner," he said.

"Delighted, madam." Muir was bemused.

"I've explained the situation to her briefly," said Chubb, "and she says..."

"Going once for three thousand...," the auctioneer cried.

"She says she's prepared..."

Muir had no time to listen. "Do I let it go?" he asked desperately.

"Going twice for three thousand..."

"Put your bid in," shouted Chubb. Muir's hand shot up.

"Going thr... - No, I have five hundred here. I have five hundred. It's at three thousand five hundred now - thank you sir." The auctioneer nodded to Muir.

"Thank *you*, madam," said Muir to the lady.

"I couldn't see this opportunity lost, Mr Muir," she said leaning across to him.

"Three thousand five hundred. Any advance on three thousand five hundred? Going once - going twice - gone, at three thousand five hundred!" The hammer came down at last, and Muir felt he could breathe again. "In the name of?" said the auctioneer.

Cross on Gibbet Hill, Hindhead

"In the name of Methuen," said Muir loudly.

"To Mr Methuen. Thank you."

Chubb whistled. "That was a close shave."

"What was it you were saying just before I bid?" asked Muir.

"I was saying that Mrs Thackeray Turner agreed to guarantee an additional £500."

"It was fortunate the bidding stopped at that point," Mrs Turner added, "because I don't think I could have gone further."

"As it is we are still some £700 short in our guarantees," said Muir, "but I have no fear we can find that sum."

"I'm glad to hear it," said Chubb. "I look forward to seeing a new property added to the National Trust in due course."

Muir sat back in his chair. "And I too, Mr Chubb. The end of a battle, I believe - Hindhead is saved!"

Hindhead Safe

The 'Surrey Advertiser' of 4th November 1905, under the headline "Hindhead Safe," declared that the Hindhead Commons, Gibbet Hill and the Devil's Punch Bowl would from now on be "preserved in perpetuity for ever."

The guarantors had met in Haslemere the previous week, and approved the bid. The committee, led by Sir Robert Hunter, raised the extra money needed, and the acquisition took place on 30th December 1905.

The land was conveyed to the National Trust on 22nd March 1906, a local committee being formed to take over the management of the commons from the guarantors, and at their first meeting they appointed Sir Robert Hunter as their chairman.

Epilogue

Sir Robert retired from the Post Office at the end of July 1913. As well as fighting for nearly 45 years to preserve open spaces and places of beauty, he had also masterminded the acquisition of the private telephone companies for the state on behalf of the Post Office. In this he was responsible for passing about fifty Acts through parliament - no mean feat.

Unfortunately his retirement did not last long, and he died of septicaemia less than 4 months later at his home in Haslemere. His funeral in the parish church and a simultaneous memorial service in London were attended by many lords and knights of the realm.

Hunter's memorial stone, Waggoners Wells

Sir Robert Hunter

A Memorial to Hunter

The Great War prevented a memorial being set up for Hunter until 1919, some six years after his death, when the National Trust acquired Waggoners Wells near Grayshott with money provided by public subscription.

An inscribed stone of Iona granite now stands solid in his memory beneath the trees near the top pond.

Appendix I. Calendar of Events

1851 Sir William Erle has Cross erected on Hindhead *(see photograph p.46)*

1855 Inspector William Donaldson killed in Haslemere by navvies [July 28]

1856 Extensive enclosures of the common lands neighbouring Haslemere
     Jonathan Hutchinson marries Jane Pynsent West

1859 Portsmouth Railway through Haslemere opened to passengers [Jan 1]

1860 John Tyndall climbs the Matterhorn (one of earliest ascents)

1862 Anne Gilchrist living in *Brookbank*, Shottermill

1863 Hutchinson and Hughlings Jackson visit Frensham and Hindhead
     Hutchinson elected full surgeon to the London Hospital

1864 James Stewart Hodgson comes to Haslemere
     First edition of Surrey Advertiser printed [Apr 3]

1865 Commons Preservation Society (CPS) founded by George Shaw Lefevre
     Robert Hunter takes his degree at University College, London

1866 Hunter's was one of the best six essays on "Commons and the best means of preserving them for the public."
     Hutchinson makes his summer home in the Haslemere area at *Inval*
     The Tennysons visit Anne Gilchrist, looking for local property [Sept 16]

1867 Hodgson buys the Lythe Hill Estate
     The Tennysons rent Grayshott Farm *(now Grayshott Hall)* [late Mar]
     Article on 'A Visit to Haslemere Fair' - describes it as 'cheerless', and the town still without gas lighting [*Surrey Advertiser - May 18*]
     Hunter articled to firm of London solicitors

1868 Tennyson lays foundation stone at *Aldworth* [April 23]
     Hunter appointed Hon. Solicitor to the Commons Preservation Society
     Haslemere becomes independent parish by separation from Chiddingfold

1869 Anne Gilchrist leaves *Brookbank* (George Eliot arrives in 1871 to complete *Middlemarch*)
     Hunter marries childhood sweetheart Emily Browning
     First gas lighting in Haslemere

1870 Penfold's plans for St Bartholomew's Church begin [July 25]

1871 St Bartholomew's Church rebuilding completed [July]

1872 Hunter's first wife dies in childbirth
     Hutchinson's father dies - property divided among his children

1874 Hunter's Epping Forest case concluded
     William Allingham marries Helen Paterson [Aug 22]

1875 Hutchinsons move permanently to Haslemere

1876 Tyndall marries Louisa, eldest daughter of Ld Claud Hamilton [Feb 19]

1877 Hunter marries secondly Ellen Cann

1881 Allinghams move to the largest house in Sandhills, near Witley [June]

1882 Queen Victoria declares Epping Forest open as a public park [May 6]
     Hunter recommended for position of legal adviser to the Post Office
     Percival Birkett takes over as Hon. Solicitor to the CPS

1883 The Tyndalls move into their hut at Hindhead
     The Hunters come to live at *Meadfield*, Three Gates Lane, Haslemere
     Hardwicke Rawnsley seeks co-operation of Hunter in appeals against another projected lakeside railway

1884 Tennyson accepts peerage reluctantly [Jan]
     Hutchinson's youngest son Bernard, aged 9, dies of tetanus in London - buried in Haslemere [Apr]
     Marriage of Hallam Tennyson to Audrey Boyle [June 25]
     Battle lost to save Sayes Court at Deptford
     Address by Hunter on "three distinct perils" - he proposes here the creation of what became the National Trust [Sept]
     Shaw Lefevre becomes Postmaster General (succeeding Fawcett) [Nov 7]
     Haslemere Commons Committee of CPS formed [Dec 16]
     The Tyndalls spend first night in their new house at Hindhead [Dec 22]

1885 Letter from Octavia Hill to Hunter states her preference for the word "Trust" - Hunter pencils in the words "?National Trust" [Feb 10]
     Hunter joins Reform Club - proposed by Henry Fawcett before he died
     Hutchinson buys land at Hindhead and builds *Trimmer's Wood* there

1886 Lionel Tennyson dies of jungle fever on voyage home from India
     Tyndall tells Huxley about 'colony of heathens' at Hindhead [May]

1887 Hutchinson's second daughter (Ethel) marries Allen Chandler Jnr [Jan]

Tyndall's resignation from Royal Institution accepted [March]

Hutchinson publishes work on syphilis

Queen's Golden Jubilee - Allinghams view parade from War Office
- bonfire on Hindhead 'burns all night' [June 21]

Hutchinson's wife dies - buried next to Bernard in Haslemere [Aug 6]

Hutchinson's first grandchild born (Allen "Rex" Chandler) [Nov]

1888 Hutchinson begins his Educational Museum at *Inval*

Octavia Hill persuades CPS to extend its campaign to footpaths [Jun 15]

Allingham thrown from his pony - never fully recovers [Sep 14]

The Allinghams leave Sandhills - move to London [Dec 11]

1889 Octavia Hill laments that "Mr. Shaw Lefevre does not rise to the idea of
the new society"

Whitaker Wright returns to England from America

Hodgson is largest landowner in Haslemere area

Tennyson writes *Crossing the Bar*

Allingham dies - Helen returns to Surrey, invited by Tennyson [Nov 18]

1890 Tyndall speech in Haslemere against Gladstone and Home Rule [Apr 17]

Helen Allingham paints Tennyson - at the height of her popularity [Apr]

1891 Letters in national press about Tyndall's screens [Sept]

1892 Alfred Lord Tennyson dies at Aldworth [1.35 am, Thurs 6th Oct]

1893 Rawnsley appointed Honorary Canon of Carlisle Cathedral

Several properties come up in the Lake district
- Rawnsley contacts Hunter and Octavia Hill again

Hunter, Hill and Rawnsley meet in the offices of the CPS [Nov 16]

Tyndall dies of accidental Chloral poisoning by his wife [Dec 4]

1894 Hunter knighted for work connected with the Post Office [Jan]

Hodgson's estates auctioned due to his financial problems
- Hutchinson buys Half Moon Estate and starts developing it [July 14]

Duke of Westminster chairs meeting to form The National Trust [July 16]

Hunter proposed as Chairman of first Haslemere Parish Council [Dec 8]

1895 First meeting of Haslemere Parish Council - Hunter in chair [Jan]

The National Trust registered under the Companies Act [Jan 12]

First lecture given in the new Haslemere Museum [Sunday 18th Aug]

1896 Conan Doyle takes *Grayswood Beeches* at Hindhead for the summer [July]

1897 Diamond Jubilee year - the population of Haslemere reaches 2,000

Whitaker Wright one of the six "Men of Millions" (*FT*)

Flora Thompson comes to Grayshott as assistant postmistress [Sept]

1898 Conan Doyle moves to *Undershaw* [October]

George Bernard Shaw first comes to district on honeymoon

1899 Report on 'despoilation' of Hindhead (*Surrey Advertiser*)
- Whitaker Wright new lord of the manor [May 13]

Hodgson dies [July]

1901 Queen Victoria dies, and Tyndall's screen finally falls [Jan 21]

Public examination of Wright ordered - he goes to live in Paris [Dec]

1902 Wright 'bolts' for the USA under an assumed name
- arrested on landing [Mar]

Conan Doyle drives his new Wolseley from Birmingham to Hindhead
and in same year is knighted for supporting the Government on Boer War

1904 Whitaker Wright commits suicide at court in London [Jan 26]

Shaw Lefevre created Baron Eversley - elected president of CPS

1905 Local decision taken to purchase Hindhead Common [Oct 14]

Hindhead Common purchased at auction in Godalming [Oct 26]

1906 Hindhead Common conveyed to the NT [Mar 22]

1907 NT becomes a statutory body legalised by Act of Parliament

1908 Hutchinson knighted for his services to medicine [June]

————————

1913 Hutchinson dies peacefully - buried next to wife and son in Haslemere
churchyard - "A man of hope and forward-looking mind" [June 23]

Hunter retires from the Post Office [July 31]

Hunter dies of septicaemia - buried at Haslemere parish church [Nov 6]

1919 Waggoners Wells acquired by NT and dedicated to Hunter [Dec]

Appendix II. Biographies

Allingham (née Paterson), Helen (1848-1926)

The eldest of six children. Her father was a doctor, and until his death in 1862 they lived in Cheshire. The family then moved to Birmingham where she attended the School of Design. Went to live in London in 1867 with her maternal aunt. Studied at the Female School of Art, then in 1870 attended R.A. schools and was taught by Millais. Went to the Slade in 1872. She was one of the very few women journalists in London at the time. Illustrated Hardy's *Far From the Madding Crowd* in 1874. He fell in love with her, but she announced her engagement to the poet William Allingham (*q.v.*), 25 years her senior, whom she married in the same year. After William's death in 1889 she returned to Surrey, invited by the Tennysons.

Allingham, William (1824-89)

Born in Ballyshannon, the eldest child of five. Worked as a customs official, first in his native Ireland, then in England. Read widely and incessantly, keeping abreast of current literature and in close touch with the output of many of his contemporaries. Sent his first volume of verse to Tennyson in 1850, and met him in 1851. Married Helen Paterson in 1874. They lived first in London, then moved to Sandhills, near Witley in 1881. He became a tireless campaigner against local enclosures. Injured falling from his pony in 1888, he never fully recovered. They moved back to London, where he died the following year.

Donaldson, William (c.1811-55)

A Scot, one of the original 'peelers' in London, who after many years police service joined the newly formed Surrey Police Force in 1851. An Inspector at Haslemere in 1855, he was the first officer of the Surrey force to be killed on duty when felled by a railway navvy in Haslemere High Street.

Conan Doyle, Arthur (1859-1930)

Came to live in Hindhead in 1897 for his wife's health, and had *Undershaw* built. Here he 'revived' Sherlock Holmes, and also became involved in local sporting activities. Described as 'a man with a hand that grips you heartily and, in its sincerity of welcome, hurts.' He served as a physician in the 2nd Boer War, and his pamphlet justifying Britain's action earned him a knighthood in 1902. He was one of the first motorists in the area, and in the same year bought a 10HP Wolseley and drove it himself from Birmingham to Hindhead. His wife died in 1906 and is buried in St Luke's, Grayshott, churchyard. A year later, he re-married and moved from the area.

Etheridge, Rev Sanders (1835-1912)

Was first Rector of Haslemere when it became an independent parish in 1868 by separation from Chiddingfold. Approved Penfold's plans for major changes to St Bartholomew's church. Proposed Hunter in 1894 to be chairman of the first Haslemere parish council. His wife, Ada, died in 1893, and he retired in 1897, being succeeded by George Aitken.

Fawcett, Henry (1833-84)

Blinded by his father in a shooting accident in 1858, he became professor of Political Economy at Cambridge in 1863 and was elected Liberal member for Brighton in 1865. He insisted on full discussion of enclosure Bills in Parliament, and became a leading member of the Commons Preservation Society. He married Millicent Garrett in 1867. As Postmaster General from 1880-84, he introduced postal orders and the parcel post, and took on Hunter as his legal adviser in 1882.

Fawcett (née Garrett), Dame Millicent (1847-1929)

Younger sister of Elizabeth Garrett Anderson (the first English woman doctor), Millicent became famed as a suffragette and educational reformer. Married to Henry Fawcett in 1867. She was founder of Newnham College, Cambridge, in 1871.

Gilchrist (née Burrows), Anne (1828-85)

Married Alexander Gilchrist in 1851. When he died in 1861, she finished his *Life of Blake*, publishing it in 1862. During this period, she came to live in Shottermill, near Haslemere, (in a house *Brookbank* later rented by George Eliot while completing 'Middlemarch' in 1871). Visited by the Tennysons in 1866, she found *Grayshott Farm* for them to rent while they bought land and built *Aldworth*.

Hill, Octavia (1838-1912)

Eighth child of James Hill and Caroline Southwood Smith. Within 2 years of her birth, her father was declared bankrupt, from which she learnt the virtues of economy. From 1855, tutored in art and introduced to social welfare projects by John Ruskin, with whom she may have had a romantic attachment - but this was shattered by 1875 when he failed to support her plans to save Swiss Cottage Fields. She joined the Commons Preservation Society and became active in supporting opposition in Parliament to further enclosures, but suffered a complete mental breakdown in 1877. Cared for by her friends, in particular Harriet Yorke, she recovered. In 1884 her attempts to save Sayes Court, and its eventual loss, led Hunter to formulate the ideas which ten years later became the National Trust. She died aged 74 of lung cancer in 1912. Hydon's Heath and Hydon's Ball are dedicated to her memory.

THE MAN FOR THE POST.

Henry Fawcett, inventor of the Parcel post

Hodgson, James Stewart (1827-99)

Came to Haslemere in 1864 and made it his home by buying the Lythe Hill Estate in 1867, and *Denbigh House* in 1868. The latter he pulled down and built *Lythe Hill* in Tudor style. He acquired the manors of Godalming and Haslemere, becoming the largest landowner in the immediate vicinity. He associated himself with the welfare of the village (as he always liked to think of Haslemere), and lifted it from the lethargy into which it had sunk since the first Reform Bill disenfranchised it. When the company of Baring, in which he was a partner, failed late in his life, he faced the disaster boldly, sold nearly all his estate, and retired to *The Manor House*, sustained by his devoted wife Gertrude.

Hunter, Robert (1844-1913)

Born in Camberwell, first child of Robert Lachlan Hunter and his wife Anne. Attended Grammar school, then went to University College, London where he gained B.A. Honours with firsts in Logic and Moral Philosophy. Here he also developed a love of walking and climbing. Encouraged by his father, he enrolled as an articled clerk with a firm of solicitors in Holborn, but he found the work totally uninteresting. To relieve the boredom he read for a Master's degree in his own time. In 1866, Sir Henry Peek offered prizes of £400 for essays on *Commons and the best means of preserving them for the public*. Hunter wrote one of the six best entries, and when a vacancy came up in 1868, the Commons Preservation Society made him their Honorary Solicitor. Here he achieved many successes in saving common land from enclosure, most notably Epping Forest, which Queen Victoria declared open as a public park in 1882. In that same year, he was recommended for the position of Legal Adviser to the Post Office, where he stayed for the rest of his working life, though he still regularly assisted the Society in its work.

In 1883, he and his family moved to Three Gates Lane, Haslemere, where he joined the growing band of rail commuters employed in London. The following year, Octavia Hill enlisted his help in trying to save Sayes Court in Deptford. The owner wanted to give the property to the nation, but no organisation existed to accept the gift. Hunter felt a new 'Company' should be established for such purposes, and so began his idea of a 'National Trust.' The idea lay dormant for nearly 10 years until 1893, when Hardwicke Rawnsley sought help to buy some land in the Lake District which was under threat from speculators. This time the seed grew, and in January 1895 the National Trust was founded, with Hunter as its first chairman. Knighted the previous year for his services to the Post Office, he also became chairman of the first Haslemere Parish Council, formed in the same month as the Trust. This diligent, quiet man retired from the Post Office at the end of July 1913, but by early November had died of septicaemia. Waggoners Wells, near Grayshott, was acquired by the Trust in 1919 and dedicated to his memory.

Hunter (née Cann), Ellen (Nellie)

Married to Robert in 1877, five years after his first wife died in childbirth. They had three daughters, Dorothy, Winifred and Margaret.

Hutchinson (née West), Jane (1835-87)

Married to Jonathan in 1856, they had 10 children: Elizabeth, Jonathan, Ethel, Proctor, Llewellyn, Roger, Herbert, Ursula, Agnes, and Bernard. In 1884, Bernard died tragically of tetanus at the age of 9 after grazing his knee while playing in their London garden. Jane never really got over this, and died herself three years later.

Hutchinson, Jonathan (1828-1913)

Born in Selby, Yorkshire, of a Quaker family, he married another Quaker, Jane Pynsent West, in 1856. He first visited Frensham and Hindhead on a walking holiday in 1863, the same year that he was elected a full surgeon to the London Hospital. This post required him to live near the hospital during the week, but the railway allowed him and his family first to rent, and finally buy, property in the Haslemere area. After his wife's early death, Jonathan, always a keen educationalist, involved himself in a project to create an Educational Museum in Haslemere - it still exists to this day in much the same form as he envisaged it then. He was knighted in 1908, and died peacefully in the library at *Inval* in 1913.

Penfold, John Wornham (1828-1909)

Born in Haslemere, he studied architecture and surveying in London and was appointed surveyor to the Goldsmiths' Company. The opening of the railway in 1859 allowed him access to his old home at Courts Hill. In 1866 the post office introduced a road-side pillar box of his design (*see opposite*). He planned the reconstruction of Haslemere Parish Church in 1870-71, and was also a diligent collector and photographer of Haslemere history.

Pollock, Frederick (1845-1937)

Born in London, educated at Eton and Cambridge, and called to the bar in 1871. He moved to Hindhead in 1884, building *Hindhead Court* (now part of the *Royal School*). Succeeded his father as 3rd baronet in 1888. Instrumental in opening and naming the *Fox & Pelican* in Grayshott as a 'Refreshment House' in 1899. Left the district in 1904 considering it had become too crowded. Shortly before his death in 1937, he advised on the form of the Abdication Act.

Rawnsley, Hardwicke Drummond (1851-1920)

Born in the old rectory at Shiplake-on-Thames. Tennyson was a distant relation and close family friend, and was married by his father in the year before Hardwicke was born. His mother had been brought up as the ward of her uncle, the arctic explorer Sir John Franklin. He followed his father and grandfather into the church, and worked as a priest among the poor in Seven Dials alongside Octavia Hill. He drove himself too hard, suffered a nervous breakdown. and was sent for a period of rest to the Lake District. This gave him a love for that region which he never lost. He spearheaded a number of campaigns against the building of railways and other works injurious to the countryside there, and in seeking the help of Hill and Hunter in these, the three of them achieved the implementation of the latter's idea of a National Trust.

Shaw, George Bernard (1856-1950)

First contact with Hindhead was in 1898, while on honeymoon. He stayed at *Pitfold*, and later in the year rented *Blencathra* (now St Edmund's School) where he lived until leaving the district in 1900 due to its remoteness from London. Supported Pollock in the *Fox & Pelican* 'Refreshment House' experiment at Grayshott.

Shaw Lefevre, George John (1832-1928)

Born in London, and MP for Reading 1863-85, he served in Liberal ministries in 1881-84 and 1892-95. Was instrumental in forming the Commons Preservation Society in 1865, and was its chairman for many years. Recommended Hunter for the job of legal adviser to the post office, and succeeded Henry Fawcett as Postmaster General (1884-85), introducing the sixpenny telegram. Created Baron Eversley in 1906.

Tennyson, Alfred (1809-92)

Born in 1809, he established his fame as a poet in 1842 and succeeded Wordsworth as Poet Laureate in 1850, the same year that he married Emily Sarah Sellwood. Made their home on the Isle of Wight, but by 1866 he was becoming frustrated with the tourists who came there to seek him out, and started to look for some secluded property on the mainland. He spent the summer of 1866 in this area, and the following year rented *Grayshott Farm* (now *Grayshott Hall*), staying there while he found and purchased suitable land on Blackdown. Here he had *Aldworth* built to his own design, laying the foundation stone on 23rd April 1868. In 1884 he reluctantly accepted a peerage. He died peacefully at *Aldworth* in 1892.

Thompson (née Timms), Flora (1876-1947)

Moved to various locations while working for the post office after leaving her native Oxfordshire, and arrived in Grayshott as assistant postmistress and telegraph operator in 1897. She stayed until the Hindhead post office was opened in 1901, whereupon business dropped by 80% and she was moved on again. Her time in Grayshott before leaving the area is recorded in her book *Heatherley*, written near the end of her life and somewhat in the style of her more famous trilogy *Lark Rise to Candleford*.

Tyndall, John (1820-93)

Born in Co. Carlow, Ireland, he found employment in the Ordnance Survey in 1839. Moved with them to England in 1842, then quitted to become a Railway engineer. In 1847 he started an academic career, and rose to become one of the foremost physicists of his time, being made a fellow of the Royal Society in 1852. His interest in the Alps began in 1856 - he was one of the first to climb the Matterhorn, and the first up the Weisshorn in 1861.

Replica of a 'Penfold' pillar box of 1866, Haslemere

He married Louisa in 1876. They moved to Hindhead in 1883 for reasons of his health, living in a single-room hut "surrounded by the purplest of purple heather" while *Hind Head House* was being built. Later he erected 40ft high screens to shield himself from neighbours. He was prescribed magnesia and chloral for his gout. Louisa administered these to him, but in December 1893 accidentally gave him 10 times the proper dose from the wrong bottle, which proved to be fatal. He lies buried in Haslemere churchyard.

Tyndall (née Hamilton), Louisa (1845-1940)

Eldest daughter of Lord Claud Hamilton and Lady Elizabeth Proby, she married John Tyndall in 1876 and devoted herself to assisting him with his work. It was a joke between them that they were both people of untidy habits. They kept promising each other to start writing 'their' biography, but mortified by her involvement in John's death, she was unable to complete it herself.

Wright, Whitaker (1845-1904)

One of a large Cheshire family, he crossed the Atlantic in 1866 as a professional assayer and began mining. Had a near scrape with Indians in Idaho - some of his workers were killed, but he had endeared himself to a squaw by giving her tobacco, so was spared. Became a naturalised American, married and had 3 children. Had 'some trouble with his companies' and returned to England in 1889, no longer a millionaire, but solvent. In 1897, the FT included him among their 'Men of Millions' again. By 1899 he had bought Lea Park (*now Witley Park*) and Hindhead Common. He began to have more company trouble, and by 1902 was asked to answer in court. He 'bolted for New York' but was arrested on landing and sent back to the UK to face charges of serious fraud. The case went against him, and he committed suicide, swallowing a cyanide capsule.

Illustrations and Maps

Chapters

Acknowledgements

The following general texts were consulted:

Anne Gilchrist, Her Life And Writings, ed. Herbert Harlakenden Gilchrist (1887)

Alfred Lord Tennyson - a memoir, Hallam Tennyson (1897)

Hindhead, or the English Switzerland, Thomas Wright (1898)

William Allingham - a diary, Helen Allingham & D Radford (1908)

Bygone Haslemere, ed. E.W. Swanton, aided by P Woods (1914)

Life and Work of John Tyndall, Prof. A S Eve and C H Creasey (1945)

The Life and Letters of Jonathan Hutchinson, Herbert Hutchinson (1946)

Heatherley, Flora Thompson (1946)

Haslemere in History, G.R. Rolston (1956)

Haslemere 1850-1950, G.R. Rolston (1964)

Heretofore in Haslemere, Allen ("Rex") Chandler (1965)

Albert's Victoria, Tyler Whittle (1972)

Grayshott, J.H. Smith (1978)

The Hero of Haslemere - Murder of Inspector Donaldson, J.S. Harwood (1984)

'Fraudsters' - Six Against The Law, Michael Gilbert (1986)

Founders of the National Trust, Graham Murphy (1987)

Letters from the Hunter files in Surrey County Record Office

Newspaper cuttings at Haslemere Museum and Surrey Local Studies Library

Illustrations and Maps:

All from the archives of Haslemere Museum, except:

Lefevre (p. 11) and Fawcett (p. 51) - *Post Office archives, Crown Copyright*

Modern map of the area, View from Blackdown (p. 22), Flora Thompson (p. 42), Cross on Gibbet Hill (p. 46), Hunter's memorial stone (p. 47) and Penfold's pillar box (p. 53) - *the author*

Design for "Balance of Trust" scales at frontispiece - *Thelma Ede*

Lea Park (p. 40) and Whitaker Wright (p. 44) - *Mrs E Harley*

The Devil's Punch Bowl (p. 14) - *Anthony Williams*

Octavia Hill (p. 13) and Hardwicke Rawnsley (p. 28) - *The National Trust*

People:

For their ready help, encouragement and enthusiasm with this project, I should like in particular to thank the following:

Diana Hawkes, Curator of Haslemere Museum, and her staff

Thelma Ede for assistance in historical research

Carol Hawkins, National Trust Southern Region Centenary Co-ordinator

John Janaway and his staff at the Surrey Local Studies Library, Guildford

Author's Note

This is not an apology, but by way of explanation I should point out that this is 'the book of the play.'

In writing the play I had to dramatise real events - put words into actors' mouths which the historical characters almost certainly did not say, and arrange scenes to show audiences a story covering some 50 years in the space of about 100 minutes.

Those who know the full historical facts will find many points at which my story compresses, but hopefully does not contradict, the truth. I trust they will understand. I hope, at least, that they will agree the work gives an entertaining introduction to the personalities and events associated with this period of history.

Those who wish to know more may spend many happy hours sifting, as I did, through books and documents in libraries and record offices to add to the story themselves.

The idea for the play "A Balance of Trust" came originally from Tony Grant, National Trust Warden at Frensham Little Pond, in 1994. It was endorsed by the Southern Region of the National Trust at Polesden Lacey as part of their Centenary celebrations, and supported as a local project by Haslemere Museum, where it was first performed, and by Waverley Borough and East Hampshire District Councils.

The publication of this book is a private venture by the author, supported in part by East Hampshire District Council.